RA ...WITH DEATH

RACE WITH DEATH

Vahida Demirović

Illustrated by Zlatan Filipović

Ta-Ha Publishers Ltd.
1, Wynne Road
London SW9 0BB

Published in March 2000

Published by:

Ta-Ha Publishers Ltd.
Unit 4, The Windsor Centre, Windsor Grove,
West Norwood, London SE27 9NT
Tel: 020 7737 7266 • Fax: 020 7737 7267
e-mail: sales@taha.co.uk • **www.taha.co.uk**

By: Vahida Demirović
Illustrated by: Zlatan Filipović

A catalogue record of this book is available from the British
Library.

ISBN 1 84200 005 5

Printed and bound by:

De-Luxe Printers Park Royal, London NW10 7NR
Website: www.de-luxe.com
Email: printers@de-luxe.com

IN MEMORY OF MY MOTHER WHO TAUGHT ME
THE LOVE OF BOOKS THROUGHOUT HER LIFE
AND INFLUENCED ME TO KEEP ON THE PATH

ACKNOWLEDGEMENTS

AUTHOR'S

This book is a remembrance of the sacrifices that the people of Bosnia and Herzegovina endured during the war of liberation 1992-95, and a reminder to us and generations to come to never forget such heinous crimes.

The English edition of this book would probably not have been published had it not been for the great support of my two children, Abid and Umihana Prguda. I would like this opportunity to express my thankfulness for their enormous support, understanding and help.

I would also like to thank the translators, the translation reviewer Debbie, the editors Mustafa and Ayesha, Zlatan for his illustrations, and the co-ordinator for MOL, Sejfudin. All spent a lot of time and effort to make this book 'closer' to English readers.

TABLE OF CONTENTS

THREE LIVES

ই঵

AS HABIBA OPENED HER EYES, her dulled sensations became
aware that the earth was cold, clammy and hard beneath her.
Her numbness made her feel as if she were in a freezing mountain stream. Slowly and carefully she turned her head and a pain shot
through her body. It was a familiar yet new agonising pain in her left
leg and like the torrents of a mountain stream, images and recollections
flooded back to her.

As she approached Bratstvo i Jedinstvo, (Bridge of Brotherhood
and Unity) on her way to Grbavica, in Sarajevo, an enemy shell suddenly exploded in her path. She did not know how long she had lain
there unconscious. The light was dim when she had opened her eyes
and she could not be sure whether the night was drawing in or the
canopy of trees was blocking out the light. The complete and com-
pelling silence around her started to seep into her bones.

As she tried to get up she became painfully aware that her left leg
had been wrenched off. Ironically, this was not the first time that her
leg bore the scars of war and that brotherhood and unity had exploded
into enmity and hostility. Fifty years ago, the very same leg which had
her now writhing in pain, had also been wounded by bullets in the
Second World War. It was as if she was caught in the eddying currents
of history, as if she had not actually succeeded in putting the stench of
war behind her as she had thought. For though she was a grandmother
now, here she was back yet again, trapped in her yesterday, lying help-
lessly in the deafening stillness.

Habiba felt entirely alone. Her mind was filled with questions: was
she dead? Why wasn't she dead? Why was nothing happening? Only

the sound of an automatic weapon shattered the silence, echoing through the valley, and even the birds flew away from the trees in panic. As the rain of bullets pelted down around her she thought there was nothing she could do. She could not move and even if the bullets did not hit her she felt she would not survive her injury. The pain in her leg was becoming heavier and heavier. I must be dying she thought.

Time passed like a slow river; the wound was cooling down. More and more it seemed to her that time had stopped and only horror was left. Yet as dream and reality were merging in the whirlpool of her mind, drowsiness lessened the pain of reality. At times, she thought it was not really happening to her. However, the cold shivers that ran through her body, and the smell of her own blood soon reminded her of reality. She knew that death was not far away. Nausea and fear spread through her and the feeling of being lost, alone and hopeless grieved her.

She had been here for one or two nights in that red pool, exposed to the rain, cold and weapons of those 'undertakers' from the hills. No water, no comforting human voice. This realisation was defeating her and would not leave her. She was also afraid of her own babbling. The pain took her to some other sphere: it was like flying above the earth, she could see the trees in the alley, then she could not see them any-more...

Then something gradually dawned on her. In the stillness around her she could see a neon sign promoting 'Unioninvest'. A word! At least that was something in this grey stillness.

For the first time she asked herself, 'What am I going to do?' The question hung in the air unanswered. She thought, now completely lucid, 'Why don't I try and help myself?'

As this idea began to come into focus, she found her senses sharpening and she could just make out some whispering. It was lost in the noise of sniper bullets, but it was being repeated. Habiba had lost a great deal of blood and her thoughts dissolved before she could absorb or comprehend what the voices were saying.

The black ravens from the hills had her in sight, they were waiting for any altruistic souls to come and help her, so that they could have their bit of fun and target practice. Becoming impatient they fired a round of bullets. Their bullets strangled the message, but not the intention of her rescuers, who continued whispering to her, 'Don't worry, we're here, we'll get you out. Just crawl towards the fence, just a little bit ...'

She had now resolved that she would not be defeated. She gathered together her strength, clinging to a thread of hope. She was determined to crawl to freedom as the soldier on the side of the fence was telling her.

She dug her nails into the ground and tried to pull her numb body towards the fence, but she had lost her energy and collapsed with the strain. She thought to herself that she had not been defeated in the Second World War and she would not be defeated now. Again she shifted her weight and though her head was spinning she slid slowly closer to the fence. The soldiers encouraged her, 'Keep going, you are almost here, we'll save you.'

Although she was fainting from the strain, she became conscious of the warm blanket, which the young freedom fighters put her on, and blissfully aware that she was at last on free territory. Alive.

Now, in our hospital, Habiba, with a wooden leg, recounted to me the story of her 'lives', for she now feels that she is in her third life. Her artificial limb always reminds her of the terror which her whole nation had to endure. Her body has to her become a symbol of her nation's persecution and survival - she would not lie down and let herself be destroyed willingly.

ELMEDIN'S WISH

❧

A PAIR OF BIG, beautiful and intelligent brown eyes watched me as I entered. Curious but cautious, they were following my every move and studying my facial expressions intently. Yet a lingering sadness clouded them. A sadness which Elmedin could not conceal, however hard he tried.

He always claimed that he was feeling well, but I could see from his pensive look that he was not glad about my visit and I knew why. He was afraid of revealing too much. Talk disturbed his hidden thoughts, which he did not wish to share with anyone. He did not even talk much with the other boys in his hospital ward. Only sometimes would he let himself be distracted and listen to their jokes. He observed their games, trying, at least for a while, to look happy or to think of his situation with less sadness. At times his sorrow was mitigated by witnessing the intense suffering of other wounded boys, his room-mates.

Behind this short-lived involvement in child's play, a whole world was burgeoning, a world of thoughts, illusions, anxiety and hope. A world which to us, healthy grown-ups, was completely unknown and incomprehensible. His war story contains elements of an adult story, but in the deepest chord of his voice an emphatic note can be felt, a note which coloured the whole scale of his speech. One day, trying to draw him out of himself, I asked him how he was feeling.

'Oh, I'm fine. I think the doctors will let me go soon. Then I can go back to combat duty.'

'What was your combat duty, Elmedin?'

'I used to camouflage our bunkers, so that the Chetniks would not be able to see us.'

4

'That's very dangerous! The Chetniks shoot at bunkers all the time.'
'Yes, but they couldn't stop me!'
'They must have seen you through their binoculars.'
'Of course they saw me.'
'Weren't you scared when they fired at you?'
'No. I was angry. It wasn't fair - they were in the hills, protected by the concrete bunkers, we were in the valley below. They're such cowards, they were shooting at us when we didn't even have proper weapons. If they had come down and fought one to one then we

would have seen who the real heroes were.

'But Elmedin you are just a boy. How could you beat them?'

'It doesn't matter how old I am. I have to fight for our country.'

'Who told you that? Did anyone talk you into it?'

'No, nobody talked me into it. I decided on my own.'

'What about your father? Surely he didn't want you to be in so much danger.'

'My father isn't here. He left with a group of workers before the war, to work in Russia. Now he can't come back because the borders are closed. But if he was here, you'd see what a real hero is like. Daddy is the bravest man in the world.'

'He must be proud of you. Elmedin, what happened when the shelling started? Didn't you try and save yourself?'

'There was smoke everywhere, it was getting in my eyes. Everyone ran into the bunkers. Our soldiers shouted, "Elmedin, run for cover!" But I didn't run. I hadn't finished covering one of the bunkers. I thought I had to cover it otherwise they would keep shooting at it. So I tried to get some more mud, but the Chetniks kept firing more shells— and then one exploded just next to me.' His face clouded again, as he said, 'It doesn't matter.' He looked down angrily at his wounded hand.

I had pushed him too far and it was too late to retract. I had offended him by reminding him of his loss and he had closed the gates of his soul. Our conversation was over.

Sometimes at night he used to examine what was left of his hand. The wound was exposed because the hospital had no more bandages (they had run out a long time ago) and in any case it would heal faster without bandages. He could see the bone jutting out and the skin taut, stretched around it. It looked so pointless suspended without his hand. He touched it. He was still amazed at the space left behind where it ought to have been. At bedtimes, he carefully put it to sleep, there, beside him where it should have been. Perhaps it was like his hair, perhaps it too would grow again. His dreams were so vivid that he could actually see it grow again, the same as the one he had had, before a Chetnik grenade blew it off. And he could convince himself that it was the same as the one he had had before, the same as his real hand.

At dawn, he would wake up, wishing that his dream had not ended so soon. 'If only I'd slept a little longer, I would see some more of my real hand.' He was disappointed that his dream was a delusion and that his hand had not yet grown back. That courage for those moments had cost him a part of himself that he had never imagined could be lost. Whenever he reached out for something he was cruelly reminded that his hand was not there anymore.

He would continue his monologue quietly during the day, so the others would not hear. 'I will find it, even if it is in pieces, I'll collect it and put it in a box, so at least I can look at it. My hand, cut off by those cowards up there in the hills, hidden behind the rocks.'

'I'll also find that grenade which blew my hand off. I'll call it all those words Mummy never let me use, the ugliest names. I'll keep it in a cupboard, show it to everyone. Everyone will see what those butchers did.'

Often he found himself wondering how he could ask the first person he saw if a hand, once cut off, could grow again. He did not want anyone to laugh at him. He kept thinking that hair grows again after being cut. Yet the barber cut his hair so carefully and affectionately, whereas a Chetnik blew his hand off with blind hatred. 'Who gave him the right to blow off my hand? If he thinks he can stop me he's wrong! As soon as my wounds heal, I will go to battle again, I will...' He could not complete his thought. He had realised that his hand would not grow back. His cheeks were red. He covered himself up to his chin, so that not even he could see himself, but he had to stop pretending that underneath the covers his body was normal. He knew his cuts and bruises so well that he could no longer imagine they were not there, that they were not part of him. He himself knew, deep down, that he had been avoiding the basic facts. Loss was there, he felt it in every moment, just as he felt his own breathing and he could no longer deny it.

Facing reality for the first time he weighed up his options. All was not lost. Though he now realised that his hand would not grow back and that he was scared for life, at least one of his hands still remained. It was now even more precious, for now it would have to do the work of two hands. However, even the hand that remained had been badly damaged and the doctors did not know if he would be able to use it again.

One day, while visiting him, I could see that something was on his mind. 'What's the matter Elmedin?' I asked wondering if he would share his secret thoughts with me.

'Please Dr Vahida, can I have a pen and paper, I want to try writing with this less damaged hand.' On this 'less damaged hand', the grenade had blown off half of his thumb. I did not want to give it to him. If he failed with this hand, he would be shattered, but he was so excited by his idea that I did not want to disappoint him. I felt inside my bag and brought out a pen and some paper. He grabbed it immediately. He had put all of his being into one hope: whether he would be able to write with the damaged thumb.

A moment seemed longer than eternity and to us both the eternity was filled with anxiety. I thought centuries had passed before I saw the first shaky letters. Those trembled letters, similar to the gothic alphabet, inspired me to encourage him into writing again. We were on the trail of the same wish and hope that in his second attempt his handwriting would improve.

That wish came true - the second signature was more readable, the letters were prettier, bolder - a victory over adversity for the boy hero. We were overwhelmed with an indescribable happiness.

'Well done Elmedin! Well done!'

He was so happy, so happy that at first he could not speak, but his face glowed and he started trembling.

'You see, I can write! I can write!'

INDIRA'S GARDEN

❧

COMING OUT OF THE Children's Ward, I heard a child crying. Hearing a child cry always upsets me. I have spent so much of my life in hospitals and seen so much suffering yet somehow I still cannot detach myself from the pain I see.

I hurried to see why the child was crying and whether there was anything I could do. Through a glass window, I saw a young woman hugging the little girl who was crying. Her right leg, or the small part of it which remained, was heavily bandaged. Holding back my tears, I approached the bed unsure what use I would be. She kept crying and I could not tell whether it was because of the physical pain she was experiencing or the distressing and painful return to consciousness. I tried to call her, but there was no response. In a disturbed voice, the mother explained that they were from Boljakov Potok, in Sarajevo, and the girl had only been brought here an hour ago, straight from the operation.

'She's a good girl and she's so popular. She's always playing and smiling. Just two days ago we were working in our garden. We were planting vegetables and the flowers were in bloom. I was teaching Indira their names. She is so clever she could remember almost all of them. It was so beautiful that day. But today, our house was hit by the shelling. My poor husband was hit - he died instantly. We could do nothing to save him and my baby has lost her leg. She'll never walk again. And she loved her father so much, I don't know how to tell her that he's dead. How can I ever tell her? And where will we go? Our house is gone. They destroyed everything, even the trees and the flowers.'

I could almost see that garden lovingly tended, until today. I could

9

see Indira's little leg buried in the soft ground among the parsley and carrots, under the carnations and lilacs. I could even hear the bitter monologue of the leg complaining about the solitude and the separation from the rest of Indira's body.

'Here I am, Indira, near you. Although I'm not with you, I can see you, I want to be with you. While my live part is still with you, warms itself in your warm room or bed, I will forever stay alone in this cold and wet ground, and you won't even know how near I am, in your garden, just a few metres away. Separation from you gave me great pain, hot and sharp iron has severed us forever. It hurt me just as much as you, maybe even more. At least you will get a wooden leg instead of me. I won't get anything.'

I came back to Indira's crippled reality. I tried to distract her, to divert her attention from her pain and confusion, but I felt that there was nothing I could do, so I left soon afterwards, demoralised.

The next day, I came at the same time. I was relieved to find Indira was happy to see me, not traumatised as the day before. Her wounded leg was still heavily bandaged, but her brown eyes smiled at me.

'I know you, you came to see me yesterday. Look, I want you to see me walk again. I wish Daddy would come to see how well I can walk.'

Before her mother and I could stop her, Indira tried to straighten herself up in bed. At the same moment, her mother sprang forward to prevent her dangerous attempt, but the smart little girl evaluated her possibilities in that split second and solved the problem herself. She quit trying without a word. I was so saddened by this that I did not go back to see her the next day.

Two weeks passed before I could bring myself to visit Indira again. I found her on crutches in the Children's Ward. Her mother was with her and was helping her get used to walking on crutches. Other children encouraged her too. When she saw me she called out, 'You see, I can walk, and when I get my new leg, I'll walk just like Daddy. No one walks like my Daddy.'

She did not doubt her words. Thankfully she did not expect me to answer. She kept on chattering, but I had stopped listening. I left the ward with mixed emotions. Her optimism delighted me, but I knew it would be short-lived, for an artificial leg is not the same as a healthy leg. The scar would pinch her all her life. It would always remind her of the incomprehensible hate of a pointless war. And what about the loss of her father? Indira was still too young to understand that particular wound, but in time she would feel it. And Indira is not the only double loser in this crazy war. How many more little losers are all over Bosnia? My soul hurts when I think of it.

THE TWINS

❧

A MIR AND SAMIR grew up with their father about two hundred metres away from their Muslim neighbours in one direction and Serb neighbours in the other. Their mother and third brother died in childbirth. Their father always tried to look after them as best as he could, but the wages of an unskilled worker had never been good; so food was rationed and few new clothes could be afforded.

The twins differed greatly in their nature and behaviour, as if they were not twins. Sometimes the difference was so great, one wondered if they were brothers at all. Samir was bigger than Amir, even though he was ten minutes younger. He was irrepressibly lively and cheeky. Amir was calmer, introvert, he did not speak much and smiled even less. Despite these differences, the twins loved each other dearly and rarely squabbled. On the occasions when they did, their father had to separate and calm them down. When they did, the quarrel was usually over a ball. They had two: one made of rubber which was bought from a shop, and the other called 'raggy' as it had been sewn by their aunt from old rags.

They were inseparable. They went to school together, they would sit together and, when they returned from school, they did their homework together from the same books. Amir was a good pupil. Teachers liked him more than Samir, who was naughty and would make fun of them from time to time. Needless to say his class mates were kept amused by his antics. The teacher insisted that they should do separate homework. Samir could not see why. He asked the teacher once, 'We do our homework together, so why do we have to do it twice and waste

two writing pads?' Even now he says he does not understand why.

The war changed many things in the life of the twins. There was less food in the house and fewer pupils in the school. Then school stopped altogether. At first they were pleased that they did not have to go to school anymore, but gradually life was becoming harder for them. They were becoming bored, restless and frustrated and they could not play outside. Their aunt, who used to visit them regularly and bring them little presents, could not visit them any more because it was too dangerous. They asked their father why things were so different now, but could not understand his replies. One day some woman from the Serb house was shouting, 'All the Turks should be slaughtered!' They understood that by 'Turks' the woman meant all Muslims, but what they could not understand was what they had done to them, that they should all be slaughtered.

'We didn't do anything to them, maybe the woman is mad,' they told their father. He tried to explain the situation, but how could he explain a war that was so senseless and one sided. It was simply the way of the adult world and it was beyond reason.

However, they soon came to witness the meaning of the threats which the Serb woman made, as grenades started falling around the house.

'Those Serbs from the hills really do want to kill us,' the twins concluded and from then on they would hide at the first sign of shelling and gunfire. Their house was not very strong, so the very first shell destroyed the kitchen, the sitting room, as well as half of their only room. Their two balls and picture book, as well as the only photographs they had of their mother, were destroyed. Their father repaired the damage to the only room they had left and life continued there. They would eat and sleep there and play soldiers. Sometimes Amir would pretend to be wounded and Samir would drag him to the corner of the room to operate. At other times, they would pretend to shoot each other with stick guns, but there was not much room for them to chase each other. They could not wash themselves so often because there was no running water and their father had to bring it from the other side of the city, so they used it sparingly. In the evenings, they would hug each other in the darkness (there had been no electricity for several months) as they heard the grenades, the shooting and the snipers. Each night their father wondered whether their home would be hit again, until one evening a shell exploded a few metres from the house. The branches of the trees came crashing through the window. A shower of glass and shrapnel sprayed the air. The two boys did not escape unhurt as before. Amir's hand was blown off and Samir suffered crushed bones to one leg and in his other leg two main bones were broken.

They were brought to the hospital unconscious and were losing blood heavily. Days after their operations and the implant of metal bars into their broken bones, the twins could not sleep because they were in so much agony. Amir completely lost his appetite and began to lose a lot of weight.

Some time passed before the pain began to lose its intensity, and the twins started adapting to their new surroundings and way of life. Their father's daily visits helped greatly, his love and care was evident. His friends, soldiers from the front-line, also visited them often. They would bring presents, joke with them and try to cheer them up. The life of the twins steadily started to return to some sort of normality.

It was not long before Samir started to recover and began chatting with all the other patients, laughing and joking about everything and everyone. And since he started jumping around with the help of crutches, he has not calmed down. Yet while Samir became more playful, Amir became quieter and ever more introverted. He was almost always silent. When someone insisted upon a conversation, Amir would not respond. He simply frowned or turned his head to the wall. Very rarely could someone involve him in a conversation. Perhaps even the word 'conversation' is an exaggeration, it should be said 'one managed to establish contact' with Amir. He then followed our words and replied with monosyllables.

Amir did, however, communicate with his brother, though their communication was now taking the form of petty quarrels usually started by Samir. Having provoked Amir over petty things, Samir would then go off to talk to the other patients. He would explain Amir's nature to all the other patients and that he was smaller and weaker, even though he was older than Samir by ten minutes. This was completely unnecessary as the differences between them were quite obvious.

On one occasion while I was in the ward, I heard Samir comment, 'Since Amir lost his hand, he talks even less.' I turned to see Amir's reaction, but his face remained expressionless. He did not even frown at his brother's description. I could not tell whether Amir had not heard the remark about his hand or was strangely indifferent towards his tragedy. Either Amir buried his sadness deep or it was so great that he wished not to talk about it.

I made daily visits to the twins, but there was not much change in them until one day. When I entered their room, they were passionately discussing stories about a legendary army commander whose name or perhaps nickname was Kan. To be honest, I had never heard about him before, so I asked Samir who Kan was, and why they kept mentioning his name with such awe. To my surprise, their response to my question was a burst of laughter. Everybody in the room was astonished at Amir's reaction, for he was laughing uncontrollably. Samir buoyed by his brother's laughter continued to express his surprise about me not knowing about Kan. Then, with disbelief, disappointment and even anger in his voice, when he realised I really did not know Kan, he said, 'You've never heard about Commander Kan? Don't be silly, everyone knows Kan!' Amir laughed even louder. He was laughing so hard that his body was shaking and tears came to his eyes. It was Samir's biggest achievement and he claimed it as his own success in front of all the people in the room.

Two months after Samir's great feat, the twins were sent to a clinic in Germany in order to continue treatment. I heard little about them and saw little of their father. He kept guard on defence lines, and was always worried, as both his sons were seriously disabled at the age of twelve. One day I met him by chance and asked after the boys. With tears in his eyes, he told me that Samir's leg had been amputated too. I was shocked at the news and deeply saddened. Now, I often wonder if Samir is still making his brother happy, now that he too has lost a leg.

DOVE

ϱ☙

T HE TWO STOREY BUILDING which used to be 'Hotel Central',
a good place for drinking coffee, is now quiet and cold. Holes
and shattered windows are covered here and there with some
plastic rags and shrapnel is lodged in the facade. I look up at the sky
hoping to see a bird in flight. It would brighten my mood and encourage me, but the sky is so misty and grey that not even the birds want to
fly there. The cold, winter morning mirrors the frozen aspect of my
soul.

A bent ghostlike form passes behind me, carrying a loaf of stale
bread under her arm. The apparition walks in silence, minding the
pieces of ice on the edges of the pavement. She does not seem to notice
me and in any case does not care. A car horn from the street afar
reminds me this is a city in which people live. Yet it echoes into noth-
ingness.

As I entered the hotel I detected the odour of squalid life: smells of
food and smoke filtering through the broken windows, dirty walls and
floors. Since the war, refugees had moved into any large buildings for
shelter - schools, theatres and hotels. The lounge floor was covered in
mud and frozen snow, scraps of paper, leather footballs and old toys.
As I climbed the stairs the smells became stronger. I could hear the
voices of children playing around the hotel corridors. I turned the corner and they looked at me in wonder.

Finally I arrived at my destination. I knocked on the door. At first
silence, then I could hear signs of life. Outside, I wondered if I was at
the right address, but it was soon confirmed. A young woman opened
the door, smiled weakly, and invited me in. The room was small and

drab, its windows blockaded, its air filled with sadness. Among the three women I found in the room, I immediately recognised the one I was looking for - Dove. Not because she was the youngest, nor because she was thin and pale (so were the other two), but because they were strangely tranquil and she was not.

I call her Dove not only to conceal her identity, but also because she is like a bird; tender and small, trembling and fearful. I was disturbed by her ghostly appearance and overwhelmed with sorrow for her lost dreams and destroyed youth. She did not even look like an adult - she appeared only fifteen or sixteen years of age - and yet she had experienced so much. She seemed to be made of bubbles, transparent and pale. Her eyes wandered restlessly around the room, looking for support, but not finding it. Her body was twitching, and it was obvious hers was a deeply suffering soul. Sometimes I could see a glint of anger in her eyes. She consciously preferred people to see her angry rather than sad. She wanted people to forget her suffering. It was as though she did not need pity nor consoling for she could not share her burden. A burden not to be wished upon any human being, especially one so young and innocent. Dove had been raped and tortured incessantly in a Serb concentration camp for three months.

The first impression of meeting her was crushing. I felt close to tears and then angry with myself. How could I help her when I could not compose myself? My hostess offered me a chair and I sat down. She was trying to hide her wound - perhaps she feared my compassion, maybe she would even misinterpret it, God forbid. My compassion was weightless compared to this burden she was carrying. There was no reflection of her feeling lost and hopeless; the abyss of her suffering was too deep. Unsettled, I looked for support. I found it in those women in the room. Even though I did not know them, they somehow kept me from crashing directly into Dove's suffering, and protected me from the enormous impact of her misfortune. They gave me some strength and stability.

'She's got light fever, she's often ill,' her aunt said. Dove did not react to these words, as if she did not hear them, as if it was not her concern. Only her eyes betrayed the darkness of her pain. She was proud and tried to hide the pain. She expressed wonder at my visit to her.

'Are you sure you're looking for me?' she asked.

'Yes,' I confirmed.

'Why?' The question, painful enough for me, let alone her, created a great distance between us. 'How did you hear about me, who told you?' she asked. I could not answer. I did not want to remind her of the hard facts. She was anxiously awaiting an answer, even a little afraid of it.

'I came to meet you, to talk and get to know you,' I said.

Dove could not understand why it was necessary for us to meet. I explained to her that I was engaged in work for a humanitarian organisation and that nobody wanted to name her in public by her real name or surname, only as a girl upon whom a great evil has been inflicted. People prefer the role of hero to that of victim. I told her that she alone had to find the strength to find a better, happier future.

The conversation was filled with pauses. Her restless fingers were tapping the table. I avoided asking her about what was done to her. I feared making a mistake. Dove's reactions were contradictory and I did not feel that I was narrowing the distance. 'Evil-doings are frequent in war,' I told her. 'I'll be your friend. You can count on me in any situation.'

Despite my careful approach, Dove was still uneasy about my visit. I think it is because I came too quickly and with no preparation. In any case, platitudes do not lessen pain and our suffering is our own. Dove's aunt and her neighbours, on the other hand, were happy that I had come. They found someone that they could talk to, someone who came from another world, one which was far from their windows covered with blankets and polyvinyl. I was not a refugee. They lived as they can, as their status suggests; the status of Bosnian refugees. They lived in cold or slightly heated rooms, ate little, had no electricity or running water.

'You know how little you get from humanitarian aid, and even that's not regular. Still, what can you do about it? Dull food makes you lose appetite and children don't grow normally. You know the food we all eat. Rice, macaroni and then more macaroni and rice. I wish the war would end and then things will be fine!'

I agreed but as I glanced at Dove again, I knew deep inside that even when the war would be over it would not erase the sufferings that were endured by her and others like her. Voices brought me back to the awkward situation. I felt I had not achieved anything by coming. I was losing confidence and I had not won Dove's trust. Only silence remained. Dove dug herself into the silence and seemed to impose it on me. Only time could heal her pain, mere words could not fix it; they could not even describe it.

However, I had not come for a silent session. I came with the opposite intention, to help her by talking, and bringing her back among people. I had come uninvited, unannounced, unexpected, but I had had no choice: telephone lines do not run in the city. Now, I was at a loss both with how to continue my conversation with Dove and how to finish it. I started explaining how my humanitarian organisation were trying to help refugees by talking to them. In wartime, with no food, heat or electricity, we were all in the same situation. By talking we could ease each other's pains and difficulties. I looked at Dove. She was blushing and her wide open eyes were looking for protection from me, but why?

From the corridor, I suddenly heard children's voices raised in an argument. A middle aged man came in to tell us that children's clothes were being distributed. The women became excited, asking if the clothes were old or new and whether they were for big or small children. I sensed that Dove had calmed down, but I could not tell how long it would last. My fear was pointless as her aunt said that they had to go to see a doctor for a check up. They had an appointment and they could not miss it.

'It's difficult to reach doctors nowadays. They have too many wounded to take care of,' she explained asking to be excused as Dove was ill and really needed treatment.

My second visit came about two months later. There were frequent shellings of the city. Dove was afraid of them. I wanted Dove to get used to these as well as surprises of any kind, sudden visits too. I had no luck with the second visit. Once again, since the telephone lines had been destroyed, I was unable to make an appointment. When I arrived at the collective accommodation room, I only found Dove's aunt. Dove was away at some other collective accommodation where the refugee women and girls attended courses on sewing and knitting.

'How is Dove feeling?' I asked.

'Well, where shall I start? I'm afraid she's not very well.'

'What's wrong with her?'

'She often gets splitting headaches.'

'Anything else?'

'Yes, she gets terrible stomach cramps as well.'

'No wonder, considering what she's been through. Is she enjoying the sewing courses?'

'I am not sure. In the beginning she was a regular, and she used to tell me what she had learned. Then, everything just fell apart. I told her not to leave. She didn't complain, but she stopped going. She asked me once, "What is the point of it all?" I told her it would be good for her to learn so that she would be able to sew something for herself and the

21

children, and make some money. "What children?" she asked. "Well, when you get married and have children - your children," I said.'

'And?'

'I didn't answer, I couldn't. And then she turned her head to the window and looked into the night. We didn't speak any more that night.'

'And after that, did you speak about the course? Did she mention any friends she met there?'

'No, not a word, as if she never went there. She told me today that she was going there, but I'm not too sure about that. I think she went to visit a cousin of hers. A nice girl, about her age.'

'Is Dove sometimes sadder than usual?'

'You could say that. Sometimes she can't sleep and when she does fall asleep she has nightmares. She has bags under her eyes, but she never complains. Sometimes she cries in the night, though she says she does it in her sleep. She would probably cry in the day time too, it's only that I'm here. She needs a change, some happiness, but with the war on I'm at a loss as to what I can suggest to her. How on earth can I help Dove when we are left with no options in life?'

In life, man is confronted by hard and often unpleasant circumstances. This puts a great burden upon the soul and the weight tends to fall to the bottom and settle. The sediment solidifies with the pressure upon it, creating a reef of resistance against all future struggles. Life pushes man to make new compromises, resolve new problems. I knew that if Dove spent time with girls her own age it would bring her back to life, but she refused to see them. She left the course because of that. They were healthy; they carried no stamp of misfortune as she did. She felt she was not equal, and that hurt. As a turtle can never free itself from its armour, man can never discard his shell of fate, burdens and nausea. So how could we help her? What could we say that was not trite and unfeeling? I did not dare go and see her again.

The ice in the holes of the hotel walls is still not melting. No one comes to repair them, and I always avoid that building, in this city without birds; this city where only the car horns and sirens remind me that its citizens are still here.

THE SILENT SCREAM

ès

H
ER EYELIDS ARE HEAVY. She cannot lift them. She is on the verge of losing consciousness and feels a numb pain somewhere deep all over: in her hand, at the top of her head, at the back and in her temples. 'I've never had headaches,' Fatima thinks reaching for her head with her hand. 'If only I could lift my eyelids, open my eyes, maybe I could find out what is happening to me.' But her hand is heavy, it cannot feel, she cannot move it, as if something is pinning it down. The pain moves through her body, it hurts most in her legs.

Suddenly, she feels a dampness under her and cold. Her whole body is shaking, as if she is in a tub full of water, but strange-smelling water; the smell is not pleasant yet it is familiar. She still feels drumming in her head. The headache and drumming are intensifying, then she feels numb. Sleepiness swamps her as if she is sinking into the depths of an ocean. She continues sinking into the deep, warm cradle of unconsciousness. She has a sense of timelessness and does not know how long this has been happening. She feels as if she has floated to the surface now, but it is not water that she is in, it smells familiar...

It is the smell of blood. A thought strikes her that maybe something bad has happened to her, an accident perhaps, maybe she fell downstairs or maybe she was hit by one of those things that frequently come in from the hills... a grenade perhaps?

The pain in her head has intensified as well as the weakness in her whole body, and she still cannot lift her eyelids. Something horrible must have happened and she must find out what it is.

She hears shouts and cries around her. Her head feels a bit clearer

now. She must find out what has happened. Is it a dream or has something really horrible happened? She has never felt this bad, without an
ounce of strength in her body. Noise, shouting, human voices, car
horns, all are impinging on her consciousness. The noises become
louder, but Fatima still cannot open her eyes. She gathers up all her
strength to lift her head and to sit up, but her head feels suddenly light
and though it is only a few inches from the ground, it falls back as if
magnetised to the ground. In that brief moment, through her half
opened eyes she has glimpsed hell: a pile of massacred bodies, bags,
tables, human heads, hands and everything blood red. She droops,
feeling weak and sick. The pounding in her head becomes stronger and
stronger, as if a hammer is hitting her.

She hears voices again, but cannot understand what they were
saying. It is not a dream. It is really happening. She tries to move again

and the best she can manage is to sit upright. She opens her eyes and sees butchered bodies in pools of blood, a child's leg, and a hand with a wedding ring still on its finger. People are hurrying about. As it dawns on her that she had been to 'Markale' to buy some bread, and all these are corpses of people who were at the market with her, she screams. No one hears this piercing scream. Perhaps they are too busy, perhaps it was internal, but it is unheard. To Fatima her scream was as loud as if she was shrieking at the onset of doomsday. The scream throws her into unconsciousness.

When she awakes and the mist before her eyes clears, she finds herself in hospital. I come to see her and talk her through her experience. She is amazed that she is in hospital and not dead. When she discovers that she has lost her leg she does not react, only murmurs, 'Thank God I stayed alive for my children.'

The weight upon her soul does not lighten as the days go by although she knows that her tragedy was not the biggest. The images of butchered people and pieces of human bodies in pools of blood do not go away. She will never forget the horror. She still believes that she survived only because she did not see herself.

WAITING FOR MUNIR

❧

HAT DAY, a southern wind blew and brought the smell of spring. Munira expected her son to visit her. It was Ramazanski bajram (Eid Ul Fitr) and it was also Saturday, a day on which Munir never missed visiting his parents. By profession, Munir was a technician. He had found a job in the nearby town of Sokolac. He settled there and got married soon after. He never missed the Saturday visit to his parents, not even when his second son was born, just before the war. However, this particular Saturday he had not yet arrived and Munira wondered what might have happened to him. 'Maybe his car has broken down...maybe he's sick, or his little son is not well, God forbid!'

The hard winter had already passed and there were the first signs of spring in the air. There was a strong breeze in the afternoon, but it was from the south - pleasant, almost warm. It caressed the cheeks, blew up the chest, brought warmth and light into the body and smelled like spring in the mountains. Munira had always loved the spring. It was spring when she married and all but one of her children were born in spring. Motherhood had delighted her and now she felt reawakened with the birth of each grandchild. Somehow it strengthened the life within her as she slowly became old.

The breeze brought with it memories of days gone by - her child-hood and adolescence, then her own house full of noisy children. Now all six of them had their own families, but their lives were complicated by war. She sighed, 'I gave birth to so many children, now they have all flown the roost. I wish they lived closer by.' She did not foresee the big-ger troubles coming her way.

27

The night was falling when Salkan, son of Mujo, their Muslim neighbour next door, brought the news that Chetniks were planning to attack the village. Their village, Novoseoci, was surrounded by Serb villages. The people of Novoseoci were hard-working and they made a good living. There was not a poor family in the whole village.

'We aren't going into exile again, are we? God protect us from harm and our enemies!' Munira thought.

She must have been thinking aloud, for her husband remarked, 'Exile? Of course! That's, if you keep your head on your shoulders and the Serbs don't cut it off.'

'God forbid! Don't even think of it,' she said.

'Whether I say it or not, the Serbs have evil on their minds.'

He left the house to prepare for their move and when he returned he brought even worse news than Salkan, 'Get ready quickly! Take what you can. Chetniks are on the rampage. They're shouting and shooting.'

'Give up your weapons Turks, we won't hurt you.' She could recognise the voice of Vukola Risto, the local drunk, and other voices of neighbours in the distance. Some people had believed them and given up their weapons; their naivety had cost them their lives. Chetniks had began a process of 'ethnic cleansing' which did not make concessions - they shot people at random, regardless of age or sex.

Munira felt relieved that her son had not come to visit after all, for he could be caught and killed. He was her only son and he sat at the top of the family's emotional pyramid. She told her husband, 'Let's just leave everything and run across the creek, before they reach our house.' As they crossed the creek and climbed the slight hill, above the orchard, they heard more shots and cries of women and children, they heard commands such as, 'Don't even leave the smallest, kill 'em all, everyone of 'em!'

The houses started burning. The last thing Munira saw was the fire reaching their house and consuming all that they had worked for, the fruit of many years labour. Thank God they were alive.

After walking through the forest half the night misfortune struck, they stumbled upon a Chetnik patrol. 'Where do you think you're going, huh? This way among your own kind.' They were roughly manhandled and separated. That was the last time Munira ever saw her husband, Ahmed, again.

With a group of women and children, Munira was taken on a bus to Hresa, a village near Sarajevo. Empty buses, with handfuls of Chetniks on board, went backwards and forwards along the route randomly shooting at them when they passed by. They shot three women and a little child, who died immediately. Munira herself was wounded in the hand. Having spent the night before out in the cold, on a damp meadow, without any blankets, her nerves were on edge from the shooting and she fainted.

When she woke up, she was in a large building, a school in Vratnik, in Sarajevo. She looked around bewildered. Where was she? Where was Ahmed and Munir? She had baked Baklava for Eid and Munir always said her Baklava was the best in the world, he could wolf it down to prove it.

'We are saved!' a woman and fellow refugee told her, disturbing her thoughts.

Munira did not respond. She had stopped following what the other women talked about. Images flashed through her mind - the shouting ringing in her ears, the fire, the Chetniks shooting. It was like a nightmare she had not awoken from, and her husband and Munir were not there to comfort her. Where could they be? When someone addressed her, she replied, 'Leave me alone, I have to find them.'

'Who do you have to find?'

'Well, my son, Munir; my husband, Ahmed; and other people from the village!'

'Our men are far away...if they're still alive,' said Hafa, Munira's next door neighbour.

'How can you say that? Of course they're alive!' Munira shouted and then the conversation stopped.

Hearing that refugees from Novoseoci had been brought to the school by the Bosnian army, Munira's daughter, who lived in Sarajevo, came to see if her parents were there. She brought Munira home. Munira continued searching. She walked the streets, asking passers-by about her son, 'Have you seen my son, Munir?' Some people thought she was mad, others thought they had not heard the question properly or did not understand it. When she was not out on the streets looking for

Munir, she would sit by the window looking at the street, hoping to see her dear son. She found a place by the window which looked onto the street. She would say to her daughter, 'Now it's really hard for Munir to find me in this city, there are so many houses here. How will he know where our house is?'

Her daughter, trying to calm her down, would say, 'If they...I mean, when they arrive in Sarajevo, they'll find us... no problem.'

Munira never stopped searching for her son. She thought he might be in the army, so she paid special attention to the passing groups of soldiers on the street, but without success. She often refused her food and did not sleep at night. She would spend the whole night listening, opening the house door, thinking that Munir was calling her name. She spoke to no one but her granddaughter, four year old Mirha, to whom she told all that troubled her, not expecting any answer, but comforted by the relationship.

One cold morning, when she had completely lost hope of finding her son, something strange did happen. She saw a tall, young soldier with a cap and a gun on his shoulders. She thought it was Munir. She rushed down the stairs to the street, running after the soldier, calling, 'Munir! Munir!' The soldier stopped and turned. At once she realised it was not him. 'I'm sorry for stopping you. I just want to find my son, but I can't.'

Bowing his head, he said in a low voice, 'Madam, I have no mother. She died a long time ago. I don't even remember her.' The soldier left and Munira walked back to the house bitterly disappointed.

She did not recover from this event. She lay in bed for a week complaining of headaches. When she felt better, she tried to continue her search, but one day she fell down the stairs and broke her leg. They took her to the hospital, where she was admitted because she needed an operation to enable her to walk again. Even in hospital, among the wounded soldiers, she still tried to find her son. 'Have you seen my son Munir?' or 'Do you know my son Munir from Sokolac?' she continuously asked. Munira still hopes he will come back one day. Perhaps it is better to live in false hope than to face the reality of Munir's death in a mindless war. She has not been told that he was killed in a gun battle on Mount Igman.

RACE WITH DEATH

ề

S ALEM P. IS A SOCIABLE PERSON, always ready for a joke, has
lots of friends, and is always willing to help people in trouble - the
wounded, displaced, homeless.

In the first few months of the war his friend, who was the father of
four children, was seriously wounded. Salem volunteered for the dangerous task of escorting him from the suburban factory to the main
hospital in the centre of the city. It was dangerous both because of the
route and because Serbs targeted the hospitals in particular. He had
been apprehensive about their chances of making it, but he knew that if
he himself had been in the same position as his friend, he would have
wanted someone to help him. If friends didn't help each other now,
who would? Also he could not bear to see the distress of his friend's
family. Anyway, if he himself was to die it would be fate - he could just
as soon die making coffee at home if a shell exploded.

Salem helped his friend into the back of the small truck. His wound
was bleeding profusely and not healing. Salem tried to cheer him up but

he himself was feeling nervous. The most dangerous part of this trip was actually the main city cross-roads where there is absolutely no protection from Chetnik snipers and machine gun fire. They were sitting in the back of the truck, not knowing what was going to happen, just hoping to get to the hospital as soon as possible. And though bullets had shot holes into the plastic covers of the truck and sunlight was streaming through them, they had somehow made it to the cross-roads near the Social Security building.

As it turned out, they had arrived on stage for the main show where they would star in a real life drama. Within the first few minutes of reaching the cross-roads Salem was deafened by the drumming rain of bullets hitting the truck and the blasts of mortars falling everywhere. Salem and his wounded colleague had become the main target of the snipers and gunners on the hill, who now concentrated their venom upon this hapless vehicle. The truck skidded to a standstill as soon as its tyres were hit; the engine too had been hit. Salem covered his head with one hand and with the other he tried to protect the wounded man as much as possible. The sniper fire intensified. Salem and the invalid were pitted against the ammunition and might of one of the strongest and largest armies in Europe. They did not have a chance. One bullet hit Salem's friend in the chest. The father of four young children died within minutes.

Salem knew that the Chetniks would not be satisfied with one victim. They wanted his blood too. He also knew that the engine could burst into flames within minutes as bullets continued to pound the truck. His only chance of survival was if he jumped out of the truck immediately, but the thought of being outside, widely visible as a target for unscrupulous killers, was stopping him. He could see the nearest safe place was quite far away. But time was running out.

Suddenly, in the midst of his dilemma, he felt something hot strike his left leg. There was pain and wetness. Looking down, he discovered that his leg was bleeding profusely and had become completely dislocated from his body. It looked as if it was back to front. 'Oh no! It's my knee,' he thought, 'I've lost my leg! I have to get out of here. I could lose my other leg as well. I could die here!' Clutching his leg, he hopped out of the truck onto the cross-roads. He realised that the space he had to cross was quite wide and exposed. Though injured and lying on the ground, snipers started firing at him. Within minutes the snipers had wounded his shoulder. Quite by chance, all this was being captured on TV.

The pain was so sharp that Salem was reeling in agony. Yet he was pushed by an instinct for life. Besides the sound of gunfire, he now heard human voices. A whole chorus was encouraging him to keep going and to hurry. The emboldening voices of soldiers and passers by, who were also on the run to shelter, became an audience shouting instructions to him about where and how to move through the open spaces towards the safety of the nearest kiosk. It was more like a foot-ball match than a man's race against death.

Instructions were coming constantly, one after another. 'Crawl under the truck,' then, 'Now crawl as fast as you can. Come on! You can do it! You can make it!' The space between the truck and the cover was incredibly wide and Salem was losing strength. The TV crew continued filming his fight for life. 'I have to crawl even if they hit me again,' he urged himself. A trail of blood now followed in his tracks. At least he could see the end of his suffering: he had almost reached the pedestrian zone and the kiosk. Salem kept on crawling with a strength that surprised even him. Finally, he reached the pedestrian zone. Soldiers quickly reached out and took him into safety behind an orange kiosk. Loud applause could be heard ringing in the avenue. The camera man stopped filming, the drama had ended.

Salem had won; he had saved himself. But the Chetniks too could celebrate, they had succeeded in having his leg amputated above the knee. Salem considered his hospital treatment as very long. He tried to alleviate the frustration by smoking and drinking endless cups of coffee, but his race against death was not quite over; the Chetniks would not give up easily.

The treatment in hospital was painful and was aggravated because Salem did not have a chance to rest. Serb shelling would last the whole night, every night and so he would not be able to sleep. One night, he had been tossing and turning restlessly. His back felt sore from lying still, and he had pins and needles in his leg. He pulled himself out of his hospital bed, leant onto his crutches and limped out of the ward to make some coffee. He had not realised that the coffee would save his life. Suddenly a mortar hit the wall next to his bed. It smashed the bed and the walls. Four other rooms were demolished and several patients, who were already injured, were fatally wounded. If he had stayed in bed, not a fragment of him would have remained.

However he was uninjured this time. He laughed wistfully, 'They have no luck with me, they keep chasing, but somehow they cannot catch me, not even when I've only got one leg! If only they knew how big the applause I got at the main show were, they would have got drunk even more.' Salem was joking and then he added, 'When I get an artificial leg everyone will remember me as a famous TV star! Those Chetniks snipers who survived, and who saw me on TV, will be really embarrassed that they missed me!'

THE SNAJPERISTI

꽃

WHEN I FIRST HEARD about the assassins who killed people for money in the world's big cities, the very thought disgusted me. Now, when I think of the unpaid killers here in my own country, those foreign assassins seem insignificant. They are like children with toy guns compared to butchers with heavy artillery. The assassin from metropolitan cities is just a shadow, the distant cousin of the killers from our hills and squares and the apartments of our former neighbours.

These killers are known as 'snajperisti' and are, according to popular understanding, an imported Bosnian Dracula - a killer who kills just for the sake of it. He likes the smell of his victim's blood and is not disgusted with the stench of decomposing flesh, for his life is refreshed by drinking the blood of his victims. That is the difference between humans and non-humans.

Fehim Hamzic was one of the victims of the indiscriminate snipers. He was on his way to repair the electricity leads on the high posts, in Bjelave which had been without electricity for ten days. He did not, however, have the chance to repair them. Hearing the explosion, he had the surreal experience of watching his own leg flying through the air. Though shocked and bleeding, he was preoccupied with the poor children, who were left without electricity. How would he repair the cables now? He felt he had to recover his leg, no matter what came in his way or how hard it would be. He would need his leg to repair those cables. He took the weight of his body on to his arms and pulled himself towards his dismembered limb. He managed to reach it and grasp it, clutching it fervently, his own blood dripping from it. His thoughts

were not concerned with this. He felt responsible to help those people, for they were as much a part of him as his own eye or leg.

Lying on his hospital bed, Fehim does not complain or mourn his fate, he does not even condemn the killers. The difference between Fehim and the sniper, is the difference between an ocean and the desert - in one humanity has shrivelled up, in the other it flows refreshingly from the depths of his soul. An assassin's only measure is the amount of money he will receive for every victim that he kills and he only accepts hard currency. The snajperist, a killing machine without thought or remorse, waits in the darkness to wipe out all traces of an entire population. The victim's innocence is not important to him, he does not even know what innocence means.

On sleepless nights Fehim thinks about the leg he has lost; it was too damaged to save. He remembers the birthmark on it and the scar he had acquired during a game of football years ago. Now that leg is disposable rubbish. 'I'll have to walk on one leg and use crutches.' He wondered if they would be able to bear the weight of his big body. He had always been big and athletic; his mother used to say it was because of her home-made cheese. He knew that from then on he would hobble about clumsily. Yet he simply kept repeating, 'I had to help the people in need. My remaining leg is a little price to pay for the beauty of life.'

A week or so after Fehim left the hospital, a sniper shot and killed his neighbour Ahmed's bubbly, five year old daughter, Saida. Fehim too mourned the death of little Saida and was distressed by her parent's sadness. 'I think it would have been easier for us if the sniper had torn off my other leg. I'm a cripple now anyway. I can't even restore electricity anymore and could have got around in a wheel-barrow. Little Saida would have lived, married and had children.' With these thoughts he fell asleep and in his dreams he saw Saida in the garden, laughing and picking white lilies.

THE FIRE-FIGHTER

❧

WHEN I FIRST SAW Fahrudin after the operation on his lungs, he was just waking and started murmuring huskily. I could just make out what he was asking, 'Is that family that I took out from the blaze still alive?'

A fire-fighter's job is always dangerous, but during the war it is even more dangerous, especially as there is the added threat of Chetnik grenades, whilst extinguishing fires. 'What can we do? We have to defend ourselves,' Fahrudin would say.

The house in the city centre had been struck by a shell and was on fire. The occupants had not been evacuated from the blaze which was intensifying rapidly. Immediately a rescue team had rushed to the burning house. Fahrudin had been the first to jump into the house. He had rescued an old woman and a child, but he knew that there were still some people in there. Time was passing quickly and the black smoke was thickly choking.

In the smoky darkness he could hear a child crying and a woman's voice. He had not been sure what the woman was trying to say. She was crying for help. He guessed that she was asking him to rescue the child. He did not expect the women's second appeal to be clearer because of the tears in his eyes from the smoke of the burning furniture and the noise in front of the house. As he moved forwards, something was constricting his leg as strongly as a vice. Suddenly he felt limbs; a body pressed against him. It was a child and he could just make out the phantom-like figure of a woman lying. She thrust the child at him, putting her child's life first. Fahrudin carried the child out of the burning room. He had saved the child, but he knew his work was not

finished. The mother had to be rescued too, otherwise the two children
both under five years old would be orphaned.

The shelling from the mountains intensified. The leader of the
brigade warned Fahrudin of this double risk. Two shells landed in the
vicinity of the burning house. It was a horrible explosion and heavy
debris fell from the roof of the house, plainly indicating the additional
risk they were taking. Another shell fell near the burning house, but

not a shred of debris fell near their feet...thank God.

'Now or never,' decided Fahrudin jumping into the fire. 'Waiting could make my rescue effort futile.' Fortunately the woman was very near the door, Fahrudin found her very quickly, but she was now unconscious. Lifting her quickly into his arms, he carried her out into the fresh air. With one hand he tried to straighten her head to help her breath more easily. As he bent over her, a grenade exploded severing his arm and a piece of shrapnel hit his lung. Fahrudin collapsed.

Unconscious, he was rushed by ambulance to our hospital. He had stopped breathing and seemed to be dead. They could not find his pulse. Still, it was decided he should be taken to the Intensive Care Unit at the clinic for treatment.

'He has saved so many lives, let's hope we can save his,' said Ibrahim, a close friend.

And they did save him, despite all the shortages of supplies in the hospital and the smoke that had filled his lungs. Unfortunately they were unable to save the arm which had been burnt in the fire. As Fahrudin awoke, this barely registered with him. He was more concerned with the family he had tried to save. It was clear that despite his nausea, the images of the fire in his mind were still very distinct along with his ardent hope to save them at any cost. When we confirmed that they were still alive, an indescribable joy and a slight blush spread on the dead pale, ghostlike face of the fire-fighter - the winner in the fight against all odds.

ELEZ STREET

ॐ

IT IS A COBBLED STREET, almost as clean as a floor in one of the houses. The street is neither wide nor narrow, it brings to mind the streets of Algerian Casbahs, where you can reach through the window with your hand and touch passers by. The inhabitants of Elez Street are excellent people, true Bosnians: pleasant, quiet, unobtrusive, and single-minded. They are somewhat reserved and talk only when necessary.

Here lived some of the men who defended our lives against the enemy machetes, bullets, grenades, mortars and shells. Thirteen houses, eighteen soldiers. The kind of soldiers every army in the world would be proud to have.

Elez Street was virtually unheard of until the war, but with the eighteen fearless soldiers, it became an inspiration to us all. They defended our doorsteps without thinking of the danger or the consequences. They were well aware that they could be killed or crippled at any time. They were always together at briefings and when they went off to fulfil their duties on the front lines they joked and laughed as much as they could in those hard and unpredictable times.

One summer afternoon, in the first year of the war, a shell struck five soldiers and three children. The children were only slightly wounded, but the five men were riddled with shrapnel. Blue-eyed Enver; Muhamed, a brave young student and Sejfudin, a young man from an eminent Vratnik family were injured. A piece of shrapnel also hit strongly built Ramiz and it became lodged in his heart. It was so deeply embedded that even the surgeon's knife could not remove it. The fifth soldier who was wounded was a miner from Kakanj.

41

This miner had come to Sarajevo just before the war with a group of colleagues who were on strike. They all stayed in the Republican Assembly for two to three days and then left. He, however, found a place to live in Elez Street and stayed to defend the capital. Though he is now far away, heroic stories about him are still told, for he left as a legend. Everybody called him Kakanjac (the one from Kakanj), because he would not reveal his true identity. He never spoke about himself and had one of the most dangerous jobs, defusing unexploded shells. That is all the neighbours knew about him. If someone asked him whether his family knew what he was doing, he would only say, 'Well, that's why I came to Sarajevo.'

The day the five friends and the children were wounded they had

been in the upper part of the street. The explosion had been so power-
ful it swept them off their feet. Kakanjac was thrown towards the
lower part.

As night was falling, it was dark and no one could see him. The families, neighbours and the people from the Civil Protection Unit were
dealing with the seven casualties they had found. They could not see
him and, heaven knows why, he did not call for help. His right arm had
been very badly injured and blood was gushing from it. He tried to
stop the bleeding, but a pack of wild dogs were gathering around him.
Their tongues were hanging out and their mouths foaming, clearly
intending to lick his wounds. The pain from the torn muscle of his right
arm was intolerable. He pushed them away with his left arm, but they
took no notice of his attempts to make them retreat.

The families, worried about what had become of him, sent out a
search party with flashlights. As they approached the lower part of the
street, through the darkness they could see the pack of ravenous dogs
collected around something. As they came closer, they made out the
figure of Kakanjac amidst the dogs and witnessed a truly horrifying
scene. The pain had become so unbearable and the intention of the
dogs so appalling that Kakanjac was biting off pieces of muscle from
his wounded hand, and even more shockingly he was then spitting his
own muscle to the hungry dogs, keeping them at bay. They rushed to
save him and pushed away the dogs. They lifted him onto a stretcher
and took him to the hospital.

The five soldiers and the children were treated and thankfully survived. With the exception of Kakanjac, they remained in Sarajevo. He,
however, disappeared with the same mystery as he had arrived and no
one knows where he is. All that remains is the memory and the legend
of a fearless Bosnian. Since that night, I have been suggesting that Elez
Street should change its name to 'The Street of Heroes'.

THE PATHOLOGY OF COLOURS

۵

ISMET G. WAS BROUGHT from Nevesinje to Mostar when he was still a baby. His mother had been rheumatic and a warmer climate suited her better, thus the whole family moved to sunny Mostar. It was a beautiful city on the river Neretva. Here he used to play and jump on the river's rocky banks with his little comrades. When Ismet grew up and finished his education, these little comrades became great friends.

When he left school, he found a job in a factory and soon started progressing. He lived happily, intending to marry and settle there, just as his parents had. Families in these towns were established; they rarely emigrated to other cities or even towns. Why should they? Their forefathers had lived there for centuries and they could trace their ancestries back to medieval times. He wanted to see his children and his grandchildren grow up there too.

As a child, Ismet's parents would take him to visit his cousins in Nevesinje every summer. Later as a boy, he would go alone to visit his cousins. It was easy thanks to the short distance and regular bus service. As he grew up his birthplace attracted him more than ever and gained a special place in his heart. It seemed that he grew with the land and felt it as something alive, some kind of live force within him. He never shared his feelings about the land with anyone. Not because he felt he would lessen their value by describing them, even to himself, nor because his cherished emotions about his birthplace would not be exclusively his own anymore, but because his pride was not merely self satisfaction but an innate sense of heritage and responsibility to his family and town.

44

When the war broke out, Ismet's pride was hurt for his land was being destroyed. Buildings embodying generations of history inherited through time were crumbling before his eyes - they did not even spare the dead, shelling the graveyards as well as libraries, mosques and schools. He was too proud to leave and stayed to became a fighter for the liberation of his land. He fought in many battles in his beloved Mostar and this seemed to bring him luck. He fought yet survived unhurt, not even a tiny scratch. One day, he was sent to the front-line at Bijelo Polje, with five comrades. Shelling was constant and unforgiving but again they were lucky and escaped without losses and even injuries. However, returning from the front-line their luck ran out. All of them were caught in a Ustasha (Croat) ambush and killed, except Ismet who was badly injured. He lost his right hand, while the bones of both his legs were shattered and shrapnel went through his cheeks and broke both of his jaws. He had wounds in his back, in the stomach, head - everywhere. It was hard to find a place on his body without shrapnel in it. Fortunately, he was found soon after and rushed to hospital.

His shattered life was reflected bleakly in the desolation and ruins of the two cities in his life. He lost all his cousins in Nevesinje, every single one of them was killed. Even his pretty, sunny city of Mostar, once full of happy, contented people had turned into a cemetery and a pile of ruins. Now ethnically divided, the city became crowded with wounded, expelled and crippled people, who were pale shadows, hard to recognise because of starvation, neglect and despair.

The battle for Ismet's life began in hospital. A hundred days of pain and a hundred sleepless nights. Anxious and suffering, he was moved from one basement hospital to another, each equally windy, uncomfortable and damp. After a hundred days he was moved to the clinic in Sarajevo, where his real treatment began. They patched up his left leg as much as they could. It was like a patchwork quilt of many colours. Under this quilt, the fractured bones of his leg were connected together with wire and metal supports. When I first saw him in his hospital bed, he looked like a head screwed onto flesh and bones, held together by metal rods. Only his eyes revealed that he was a live human being.

Yet Ismet stands out from all the patients I have treated for his good nature. Whenever I would ask him how he was feeling, Ismet always replied that he was feeling better and hoping for the best. Even when his facial muscles twitched with searing pain, his eyes still glowed with some magical shine from his plum-skin complexion. Yet it was distressing to see that the red-blue tinged with mauve were the rainbow colours of disease and not the rosy glow of health. He never complained, nor were his answers coloured with dark tones. Even when he felt debilitating pain he would simply say, 'The pain doesn't last long; it'll pass soon.' He tried to hide the pain in his wounded leg, held together by iron rods and plates, so as not to upset or sadden those around him. Yet when he said, 'It's nothing, it'll pass,' the colour of his face contradicted him and showed that pain was in every pore of his body. Seeing our doubt, he would add, 'I've been sleeping, you know, that's why my face is now red...' Whoever got to know Ismet better soon discovered that he spoke from his soul. A soul which was careful not to upset the person he was talking to and not to induce pity. If he read pity on someone's face, it upset him. Pity was for women and children, not for him. His soul ached for the children who were growing up in the ruins and the basements, instead of on the river banks as he had. 'What are those poor children doing in the cellars of Mostar? They're shut up in them, instead of growing up strong and healthy in the sunshine, because they could be hit by shells!'

And now, he is in cold and distant Finland, where they sent him to continue the treatment. I think about this fragile, wounded man held together with metal rods who defeated death and refuses to be beaten by his condition. I wonder when the sickly colour will fade, but I know that the warmth of his soul will melt the language barriers of that icy land and warm the rooms of their hospitals.

COUNTING BULLETS

ॐ

O MER, A PROUD, ELDERLY MAN, guarded the local arms depot. He loved the bullets he watched over; he kept them safe and polished them. Every bullet was dear to him, not because they could kill, but because they could prevent him and his friends being killed. He was not sure if 'dear' was the right word to use, but he certainly looked at every bullet with sympathy; each one made him happy. He wanted each one to be near him so he could see it whenever he wished, touch it and be sure of its existence. As for the exact number of bullets, he often deceived himself, saying, 'Well, I still haven't looked there!' But he did not want to check, in case he proved himself wrong. As for rifles, he could not count more than there were, even if he had wanted too, as it would be obvious if he was wrong. Others could catch him lying and maybe someone would say, 'Omer has gone old and senile.' He might even be accused of theft and the matter could be reported to a high ranking officer. In his defence in court he would have said, 'Nobody loves this country and the weapons with which we defend her as much as I do.' However, that would be deemed boasting, and being a modest man and a patriot, that would not suit him. Still, if he kept silent, that would mean admitting his guilt for which he could be sent to jail and he would not like to be called a thief. Regardless of that, Omer felt linked to the guns and the ammunition. Often he counted the bullets in his head and fell asleep doing it. He would continue in his sleep until he woke up unsure of the exact figure. He wanted to be a hundred percent honest, but he could never ascertain the exact figure. Omer knew that if he talked about this, people would think he was crazy, so he did not talk much. He was not bothered about this. He only cared about the number of bullets. What really bothered him was that he felt honesty was the most important thing in his life, as he had always taught his children and grandchildren.

Omer proved himself honest when he joined the Bosnian Army at the age of fifty eight. He liked the sound of 'Bosnia' and he often rolled the word off his tongue. The word Bosnia comes from the ancient

word 'Boss', which means clear thinking on account of gentle nature - just what he wanted to be.

Both of his sons were at the front-line, where they proved their courage. The danger from the shelling and the sniper-fire grew worse everyday, both on the front-lines as well as in the city. People died everyday: elderly people, women, and children, even new-born babies, for the enemy did not discriminate.

The number in Omer's family had grown from seven to eleven, as his little grandchildren had been born. Fearing for their safety, he took his younger son's family to his flat, since their flat was more exposed to the shelling. They lived like everybody else, merely existing rather than living. There was little food, less water and no electricity at all. More and more people died at the public wells where they collected water and in the parks where they collected wood for heating and cooking and even at graveyards. The winter came and it got colder; people had to cut down the trees in the parks and burn them in their fireplace. Everyone needed warmth, but Omer did not change the way he was thinking or the pattern of his interest. He was worried but he would not say. He did not talk much. Sometimes he would sigh, 'At least we have the roof over our heads. We must be patient. It's war. The refugees have it much harder.'

His family had managed to live without major troubles, until one day an enemy shell landed on the school at Cengic Vila. It killed all the children in one of the classes including Omer's grandson, the son of Omer's elder son, Fadil. The parents of the boy were traumatised by the loss, which can only be understood by someone who has actually lost a child himself.

Omer's sadness turned his hair white, he looked at least ten years older and wrinkles appeared on his face. The fifth day after his grandson's funeral Omer reported for duty at the arms depot, where he was met by a soldier who had been on duty instead of him. Bor (nobody knew his real name) was tall and had joined the battalion after losing his brother in a battle in Herzegovina. His brother's son, Kemo, had somehow escaped from the Chetniks' knives and Bor had sent him on a convoy to Slovenia for safety.

When Bor saw Omer, he was shocked by Omer's appearance. Omer seemed strange and distant as if he was another person. Bor followed him into the warehouse where the ammunition was stored. Omer grabbed a handful of bullets and hurled them on the floor.

'I cared for you like a parent cares for his children and now you have killed my grandson. You're just bits of destructive metal and you should be destroyed.'

He sat down and started crying. He cried for a long time. Bor sat and watched him patiently and quietly waited for Omer to leave the warehouse. Wiping his tears on the way out, Omer quietly said, more to himself, 'He was my favourite grandson.' Both were stricken by sorrow, Omer for his grandson, Bor for his brother. They could not renew the memories of the dead, as it hurt afresh and eroded the thin layers of oblivion built by time. Omer never entered that warehouse again. His sorrow for his lost grandson with time became sluggish. It anchored in the bay of painful memories for the loss of dear people; in a bay where, from time to time, a wave comes and brings even more pain to the collective pain of a whole Bosnian nation.

THE LAST SON

ﻹ

'THIS IS NOT A PROPER WAR, father. This war was master-minded by Serbia and Montenegro to kill as many Bosnians as possible. It's just a cold, brutal and systematic process of elimination,' said Bajazid.

'Exactly. The amount of destruction and the murders they've done couldn't be told in a year's time. The Chetniks did the same during the Second World War - they raped women; massacred Muslims, throwing them, dead or alive into the Drina river; destroyed everything they came across. You can't think of any evil they haven't done,' agreed Adem, his father, a wounded soldier from Radovcici, a village in the district of Srebrenica in East Bosnia.

Adem was cautious. He had been staying awake whole nights listening diligently for the enemy and so far he had managed to save himself and his son. He did not want to rely on just the village guards, a duty which he himself sometimes performed. Sadly, diligent listening was not much of a defence, when one Friday, marauding hordes of Chetniks poured into the village before dawn. They were shouting and spreading terror among the villagers. Adem realised they were in grave danger - soldiers defending Bosnia were not looked upon too kindly by invading Chetniks, indeed they were usually singled out for the most barbaric torture. Any second now, they would be breaking down his front door and taking them into captivity, perhaps worse. With not a moment to lose, he awoke Bajazid, who was asleep in the same room, and together they rushed out through the back door just as noise of the mob could be heard out front. Adem fled from the village in tears for he had not managed to save his wife and other two sons who had been

sleeping on the upper floor of the house. Homeless and alone, they left their village for the first time in their lives, grieving sorely for their family. Adem and Bajazid slept in the forests at night, heading west to escape the Chetnik weapons. In the daytime they made their way by marking the barks on the trees and at night they followed the North Star.

After a week of roaming they reached relative safety and immediately reported themselves for active duty. Manning one machine-gun between them, they fought and mourned together. They had no idea what had happened to their family, but they kept their sadness from the other soldiers. They both suffered terrible nightmares and would wake up in the middle of the night, sweating, afraid to go back to sleep. Whenever they were off duty, they would walk in the nearby forest, exploring it like exiled scientists.

They scanned the groups of refugees who passed daily near their position, hoping that they might see some of their relatives, but they knew it was in vain. The soldiers felt distressed and demoralised at the sight of refugees, especially Adem and Bajazid. They were starved and pale and had dark circles around their eyes. It was hard to watch the gaunt women dragging their crying, starved and frightened children, and even worse to see the women whose children were so sick that they had to be carried. They were like strange creatures from a horror movie. The soldiers gave them whatever little rations of food they had to save them from starvation and even death. Adem and Bajazid in the midst of their desolation knew that their own suffering was just a fraction of the collective tragedy of the Bosnian people as a whole.

Bajazid was the centre of Adem's worries about the dangers that surrounded them for Bajazid was now perhaps his last son. Bajazid had shown himself to be a good and brave fighter, which made Adem happy. Like any proud father, he hoped that Bajazid would become a hero but stay alive as well. Yet, strangely, he did not imagine Bajazid dying or even being wounded, he was more worried about what would become of Bajazid once he himself died.

'What would he do without me? Who would protect him?' he asked himself often, never doubting his abilities to protect his son. He did not dare think about it.

At the beginning of winter, a tall, thin, young man left a group of refugees and joined the soldiers. His whole body, especially his back, was like a chess board, full of dark spots - clearly the victim of torture. His bruised face and swollen eyes made him look like a ghost. Suad, that was his name, lived in the hamlet of Dzafici, in the district of Bratunac. He had miraculously escaped from the infamous 'Bus of Death' - that fateful journey where those in Concentration Camps are herded onto buses, driven off somewhere and summarily executed. With a group of refugees, he had roamed the forest for five or six days,

54

until he got far enough from the slayers. He became good friends with Bajazid and stayed with their unit. As soon as he recovered a little, he took up arms like the others. Adem too came to love Suad as if he was his own son. He would remark to Bajazid, 'You must listen to Suad, he's a day older than you and like a big brother. Listen to his advice, he's more careful.'

At the end of winter, Bajazid and Suad were sent with a group of soldiers on a sortie. Adem bade farewell to them saying, 'May God protect you all. Come back to us alive and in good health.' Yet a nagging fear was tormenting him; he was afraid that the mission might go wrong, but he tried to reassure himself that everything would be fine.

His worries were soon realised. From the direction in which the boys had gone, explosions were heard and the more experienced soldiers quickly realised that these were land mines detonating. There was an alert and they went to rescue the stricken soldiers.

All around there was debris: pieces of shoes; clothes stained with blood, soil, snow and there were broken pine branches. They found many wounded soldiers, and, without stopping to examine their injuries, they transported them as quickly as possible to the make shift medical facility situated in an earth-cabin. Adem did not move; he felt as if his legs had turned to wood. He feared facing the death of his last son directly. In front of the earth-cabin, he listened to the conversation between Ahmed, a student of medicine, his assistant Osman, and the soldiers who were bringing in the wounded. Suddenly, Adem heard Ahmed say, 'Hey! This guy looks like Suad. It is Suad!' He was pointing to a soldier being stretchered in. Adem rushed towards him. Could it really be Suad? Yes, it was him. He was alive, but where was Bajazid? Suad, injured and exhausted, seeing the question in Adem's eyes, motioned towards the forest. It seemed Bajazid had been missed out in the confusion and panic that had ensued after the explosions. Adem, in an instant, ran towards the forest.

After a while, it became clear Adem had not come back nor had Bajazid. Some soldiers, realising they were missing, decided to go and look for them; they had to find them both, father and son, two fellow soldiers, dead or alive.

They found Adem lying on the ground, unconscious. His right leg had been blown off and the wound was gaping. Bajazid was lying near-by under a bush. Much later, Adem told them what had happened.

'Looking around, I saw the branches of a bush move. I knew there was someone there. I came near, moved the branches and saw my son lying there. He signalled to me that he needed a stretcher, but when I ran towards the earth-cabin, suddenly... boom! I don't remember anything after that. When I woke up, the soldiers were trying to stop the bleeding from my leg. Later, they brought me here, to the hospital.'

In the hospital, Adem often explained his vision of the war to me. Later, when he recovered, he would make jokes and try to cheer up the seriously wounded soldiers. This despite carrying the unfortunate burden of not knowing the whereabouts of his beloved wife and two other sons. Adem was thankful to God that Bajazid was not badly injured. He often said, 'If Bajazid had died, my heart would have broken. He has recovered quickly, and now he's healthy again. He'll soon join the unit again. And as for myself, it doesn't matter, I'm too old. Anyway, I can live without a leg. If I have to, I can still shoot a rifle, my hands are OK. This way, at least we're both still alive.'

SEPARATION

❧

'**H**urry up, Dzevad! Go! They're close to the house!'
'I can't go without you mother. How are you going to cope
without me? You'll have to look after the farm and a hundred year old woman all by yourself.'

'She's not a hundred, Dzevad, she's ninety-five. Don't worry. They won't hurt us old people, we're harmless. Otherwise they would disgrace their own people.'

'Let's leave together, Mama. I'll carry Nana and you can walk. Nura will take the girls.'

'Don't be silly, Dzevad...they are criminals, but I'm sure they wouldn't hurt old people.'

Reluctantly Dzevad's family - his wife and their two girls - took a few things and fled up the hill towards the rocks.

*　　　*　　　*

I met Dzevad at the clinic. He had come to the Sarajevo clinic for an operation on his frozen foot. He had been treated three times before, after being wounded in the arm and the head.

When he had left home at his mother's entreaties, Dzevad, displaced and threatened, had felt his only option was to join his compatriots in defending themselves and liberating their land. Once, he recalled, with about ten of his friends, he had disarmed a group of seventy Chetniks.

He and his unit defended the hills above Visegrad and its civilians for a while, but then the defence had to withdraw to the little town of Medjedja. Since that time Dzevad fought as a part of the 'First

57

Glorious Visegrad Brigade' at the position called 'Borova'.

However, the Chetniks then advanced and attacked Medjedja with around ten thousand troops, so the two hundred and forty defenders had to withdraw to Gorazde with a large number of civilians - old men, women and children.

He left Gorazde for Sarajevo with a group of comrades in February. The day was sunny and pleasant, and almost warm, but it took them seven difficult days to cover that short, but unbelievably hard distance. The road took them over the cruel, almost impassable mountain saddle of Rogoj which towers the mountain Treskavica. They had to avoid Bjelasnica mountain.

The whole mountain area was white and flat because of deep snow, making it impossible to notice any valleys or hills. Even the guides got lost, as they were unable to orientate themselves and to decide which way to go next. The detachment was forced to stay overnight in a mountain cabin. However, by the time they had reached the cabin, Dzevad had realised his feet were frozen, especially the right one. He could not even take his boot off, plus his frozen sock was glued to his foot. His friends held a flame near it, but it would not thaw. They had to cut through the boot and the sock. His left foot was less frost-bitten, but they realised that if he did not receive medical attention soon it would become gangrenous. So when the guides finally managed to lead the column towards Sarajevo seven days after leaving Gorazde, Dzevad was transferred to our hospital for an operation.

He was a very subdued patient - he never raised his voice, or even became upset. He gave the impression of a mild mannered, well educated man. Once, when I entered the ward to visit him, I witnessed his conversation with the patient in the next bed.

'Does your leg hurt?' the patient asked him.

'No, this frozen one doesn't, but my right arm with these multiple wounds sometimes does. It's not important though. Different people feel different kinds of pain: head injuries, amputated legs, lost sons or fathers or daughters. Everybody hurts in war, and we have to put up with it.' He shrugged his shoulders then continued, 'Many have been wounded by bullets on Mount Treskavica and I was only injured by snow and ice.'

'Did you know that tall guy from Visegrad, the one that dyes his hair?'

'Yes,' answered Dzevad in a dry and brisk tone.

'I heard he got out of the army and is living somewhere and writing. Have you heard anything about it?' the patient asked, filled with curiosity.

'No.'

'Of course, the sons of influential people can always get out of the army to go and work for some humanitarian organisations; they write something just to get out. And there's nothing to write about, believe me, the enemy is closed around us and the killing is all the same.'

59

Dzevad lost his temper and jumped off his bed. He almost fell because of his injured foot, which he had forgotten about in his moment of fury. He leaned on his left foot, grabbed a cane and rose. I saw him stand up straight and strong, and he seemed to grow bigger. Upset, he spoke in an angry voice,

'Why are you asking me that? I'm not interested in this conversation. I was a fighter from the very first day and I will continue to be as long as I have this head on my shoulders. Even if everybody 'gets out' as you say, I would never even think about it.' Angry, leaning on his cane, he walked to the window.

'If only I knew whether my mother is alive,' he said in a quiet voice, almost talking to himself. He leaned out of the window and gazed out at the snow-covered slopes of Trebevic mountain.

*   *   *

The day his mother had beseeched him to leave home, a rain of bullets started falling thick and fast from all sides. Outside in the field, it was impossible to stand in one place for fear of being shot. Smoke was rising from burning houses, filling Mevla's kitchen, making them all cough. Nearby, Saban's house was in flames. Mevla was sure she made the right decision, 'Thank God, Dzevad led them to safety.' Then she looked at her old mother and said, 'The two of us are old, and we'll have to die sooner or later anyway; nobody lives forever.' She was not afraid of dying. She was only scared of torture and disgrace. 'As long as my Dzevad and his family are safe. They are so young...' her voice trailed off. Thoughts of Dzevad's escape were swarming around her head and she could not get rid of them.

At that moment somebody kicked in the door. Mevla knew who it was - only thugs enter like that, but she was not scared, nor was she surprised. 'Is it because I've got used to danger?' she wondered. Her father had been killed in the Second World War by the fathers of these murderers. 'Or is it because I am not capable of judging danger anymore?' She realised her calmness originated from the relief that Dzevad had escaped.

'Where's your son? I want to see him,' shouted the first one.

Mevla almost did not hear the Chetnik shouting.

'He also went to celebrate and he took his rifle with him. Maybe he'll bring us something too,' the old and almost blind grandmother spoke. She almost could not differentiate men from women, and more and more spoke nonsense. The Chetnik thought she was making fun of him and shouted, kicking the wooden floor of the kitchen.

'Why are you getting angry, he can celebrate a little bit as well,' the old woman spoke again.

'Get out of my way.'

'But I want to celebrate too.'

'I'm gonna set you on fire, together with the house, if you don't get out of here right now. I hate Muslims and their houses, get out of here, now!'

Mevla realised he was capable of doing it, so she wrapped her mother in a bed sheet and led her out of the house. The Chetnik poured petrol over the tables and struck a match. Mevla and her mother stood under the pear tree in the orchard, away from the house. The house was made of wood and orange flames spread rapidly through it and the wind spread the fire to the trees. Their evil deed done, the Chetniks left jeering and cheering. Mevla watched forlornly as their house was ravished by fire. Tears welled up in her eyes as she put her right arm round her mother's waist, taking almost all of her mother's weight onto herself.

'Let's go, mother, let's go... come on, I'm holding you.' They could not walk far, but they were out of danger from the fire and her mother struggled on. Mevla's strength was waning; she sat next to her mother to have some rest. Too frail and tired to walk very far, they spent the night huddled together on the grass.

Mevla was awoken by the smell of burning lingering in the cold dawn. Her mother was already awake and shivering. 'Is our house gone, Mevla? Or is it just my eyesight?' Mevla pretended not to hear the question. She wondered if there was a wheelbarrow or a cart left in the field. She simply was not able to carry or even lift her anymore. By chance, she came across an old cart. She put her mother in it and started pushing. She did not know where they were going, only that they should be as far as possible from this hell. She did not know that hell was ahead as well as behind them.

She went back to Dzevad in her thoughts. 'If he is carrying his hunting rifle, he can catch something to eat. He can defend himself from the enemy if need be.' She remembered the day his father bought the hunting rifle for him, just for fun. It was more than ten years ago. 'You may even become a forest ranger around Visegrad,' his father used to say. Back in those days it seemed to Mevla her husband was joking, but the joke had become a nightmarish reality.

'If only Dzevad can stay alive. I buried three sons a long time ago, I could not survive Dzevad's death.' She was pushing the cart with a lot of effort, but the fact that Dzevad had escaped gave her strength. Then her mother spoke, 'What is this, Mevla? Who is celebrating so much? Do you hear it, Mevla?'

'Yes, I can hear it, Mama,' and she went back to her thoughts.

'I wish I hadn't lived to see this,' she kept repeating. She felt her head was empty. 'Luckily, Mama does not understand the situation, so she will not suffer from bad memories and nightmares if she survives.'

'Can we really survive this disaster?' Mevla asked herself suddenly. She remembered when she told her son never to kill a man, because the one who does never survives. 'These murderers are sending so many people to their deaths. I suppose their mothers never told them to respect other people and to be fair,' she thought.

By now she was pushing the cart more by will power than by strength. Suddenly, as they reached the clearing on the road, snipers from the hill started shooting. Mevla slowed down, hoping they would take pity and stop shooting. But as they walked more and more slowly, the cruel snipers shot more often at this tiny column made up of only two old women, one of them not even able to walk. They did not seem to want to finish them off right away for then they would miss out on their favourite pastime - shooting at live targets. So they continued to play this more terrifying version of Russian roulette with the old women. People on the other hill, unable to help, saw them leaving through the rain of bullets, two tiny little dots, until they disappeared into the distance, maybe even from this world.

THE BREAD QUEUE

&

'I WAS FORTY TWO when my wife and I decided to adopt a child. We had been married for ten years without having children ourselves. We had been considering adoption for a long time, and as time went on my wife became increasingly determined. She had only asked for one condition: she wanted a girl, only a girl, as boys can be a bit difficult. Night and day she pestered me, saying, "Hilmo, it will be so much better at home, our family will be complete. Children can be so loving." So one day we ended our solitude and two became three.

'When our daughter Enisa arrived in our home she was almost three. Maybe it would have been better if she had been younger, but you can't have everything. Many people search for ideal solutions in their lives and miss good opportunities. Our lives had become settled and repetitive but now Enisa's vivacity infused our lives. Enisa was a tiny and dimpled little girl. She trotted about the house giggling and she immediately snuggled up to my wife. My wife became radiant, rejuvenated at once by the girl. We saw the world afresh through her eyes. It was a real pleasure to watch her grow and learn and love us. Though I had not been in favour of adoption, when Enisa came I realised how much she had brightened up our lives. She was loveable and charming. Everyone who met her wanted to hold her. She had an even rarer talent: she loved us both without reservation and equally; she never let me feel that she loved my wife more than me or vice versa.

'However, soon after she came in our home, Enisa surprised us both by asking where her real mother was. We thought she had completely forgotten, but it was clear she hadn't yet forgotten either her mother's face, or her voice, or the warmth of her love. We didn't know what we should tell her, especially as we did not want her to be upset when she discovered the truth. In any case she was too young to grasp the concept of death. So we said that she was far away, but that she loved her very much and if she had been near she would have looked after her.

'Despite our feeling of happiness, well actually because of it, we felt guilty, like thieves, for having her in our lives. I thank God that similar situations and similar conversations didn't occur again. I still don't understand why Enisa never mentioned her 'real' mother again. Perhaps she understood that there wasn't a real mother anymore, or perhaps she had seen how saddened we had been by the question and did not want to distress us. I hope that it was because from then on she accepted us as her real parents. I know for sure I would do anything for her. And after all I owe her my life, she saved me from death.

'I can't understand how a six year old child can save such a huge man,' said Omer, Hilmo's friend who had come to visit him in hospital.

Hilmo smiled, he loved talking about his daughter and especially how she had saved his life. 'You have to listen to the whole of the story to be able to understand, Omer.'

'Well, it was on 28th May, a beautiful spring day. There wasn't much shooting that day so there were more people in the streets. It was too nice a day to spend cooped up in the shelter. That morning we decided to buy bread in the shop near the market 'Markale'. Enisa asked me to buy her an ice cream. We bought the ice cream first and I told her to run home. I joined the bread queue.

'I remember there was a lady who was buying flowers from a wheelbarrow stand. And I thought she was crazy, "People are struggling for bread and she wants to buy flowers! Who cares about flowers in the middle of a war?" Then it occurred to me that I could buy my two ladies a few flowers, as I still had a couple of German Marks.

'I was in the queue for ages and I was becoming agitated - I think it was my sixth sense. A man behind me in the queue said, "I wonder why they are so quiet today? What are they playing at?" (referring to the Chetniks' shooting). I didn't know what to answer, but it was bothering me too. The night before I had had a strange dream.

'I was walking along a long road. I didn't see anyone, not even a dog

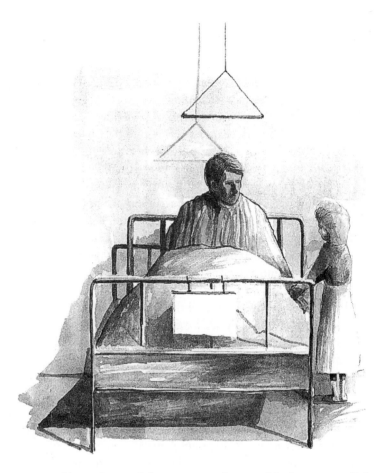

or a cat. Along the road there were no houses. No houses at all, but I don't remember whether there were any trees. Anyway, I walked slowly, but didn't know where I was going. After quite a long walk I noticed, on the left hand side of the road, an oval shaped space, not very big and enclosed with a rather tall wall. At first I thought that it was a small park. Then I thought it was a nursery garden. I'd never seen such a small nursery garden so I jumped over the wall to have a better look. I was surprised when I found myself in a graveyard. At least I thought for some reason it was a graveyard. There were small grave mounds lined up with a higher bit on one end of each mound, but here there weren't any gravestones or crosses or epitaphs. What else could it be if not a graveyard?

'And there was no one to help me solve the secret of the enclosed space with the grave mounds. And what affected me most was the silence that kept wrapping me up like the softest dressing gown and the peace I felt; I could listen to my own breathing as if it were music.

'I wasn't thinking of my dream when I was in the queue. So many things have happened during the war and if we didn't put them out of our minds, our heads would burst. I was just wondering what the Chetniks were up to, when suddenly there was darkness - then a noise, coming from far away and gradually approaching. Then sirens and the sound of many human voices. Slowly I could distinguish some voices and understand that people were crying for help. I felt damp and tried to get up, supporting myself on my elbows. When I opened my eyes, I saw people lying around as well as dismembered parts of human bodies; everything was soaked in blood.

'You know what it's like to see all that blood? You can't imagine what it is like to see so much blood. We go about our lives and our bodies are normal; we get the odd back pain or headache now and then and we complain. Then, one day you wake up and all that stuff from inside your body is splattered everywhere and the blood as well. And it is so red... you just can't understand what it's doing there.

'Eventually, I glanced down at my body. I tell you, I cannot describe the horror I went through in that moment, and I will never be able to. We take our bodies so much for granted; we assume that as we were born whole, we will stay whole, and then one day you discover you haven't got a leg anymore. At that moment, I just thought: what is life without legs? I don't want to live my life with just the upper part of my body and to be an invalid or a burden. So I lay back, closed my eyes and remained silent, thinking they would believe I was dead and leave me, and that way I would bleed to death.

'I don't know for how long I stayed there just waiting for death, thinking that my life was over.' Hilmo turned over, suppressing a groan, and drove away the images of blood and limbs scattered on the road. He laid his head on his palm and then looked through the window, beyond Omer, into the ghostly grey city.

'Suddenly an image of Enisa came to my mind. Almost aloud I asked myself, "Is she going to lose her father for the second time? No, no, she mustn't grow up without my support." I started to call for help, and, as you can see, here I am, thankful to have survived.

'Enisa comes everyday to visit me now that we live near the hospital. She fusses over me, combs my hair and feels my stubble. Sometimes she hugs me and says, "No one has a better father than me." Yesterday she told me, "You have to get better as soon as possible and get new legs so that we can buy ice creams again and go to the park as we used to, and I know lots more places to hide when we play hide and seek - you won't be able to find me next time."

'And I said to her, "You're now too big to play hide and seek, and without legs I can't search for you." But she didn't give up, she said, "You can, you can! I won't hide in a place that you can't find me."

'You know, Omer, some of us will survive all that is still ahead of us, and afterwards our names will be engraved on our tombstones, stronger and clearer than when we were in our cradles.'

THE LITTLE REFEREE

 હ

ZLATKO LOVED HIS FRIENDS and the games in which he could take part. When he was only three years old, he became very ill with a high temperature and he was left with an infirmity in his right arm and leg and some speech impediments. He spoke slowly and with difficulty, sometimes he would mix up words, going red and even beads of sweat would collect on his forehead, making it even more difficult for him to talk. Doctors could not tell if he stammered because of difficulty with pronunciation of certain words or whether he forgot in that particular moment how to enunciate them.

Zlatko's disability meant that he could not participate in many games. He would be excited whenever his friends asked him, 'Look,

Zlatko, who's better at this game, me or him?' Even more when they would choose him to be referee when they played football. It made him happy, because he thought that by choosing him to referee, his friends were giving him an important role in the game. The word 'referee' sounded strange to him and it also made him feel proud. It made him a participant in the game, albeit a passive one. Zlatko was always in the company of his friends and never felt isolated or rejected.

Due to his quiet and mild nature, the boys from the neighbourhood loved him and were always around him. They were wise never to ask him about his illness or even to mention it in conversations around him.

While outside on the street, or in the small playground, life was carefree - a world of childish games, laughter, noise, arguing, falling out and making up - in Zlatko's house everything was completely different. It was the world of silence, measured gestures and habits. Everything was organised to suit Zlatko's abilities. His parents monitored every move he made: 'Zlatko, watch your step down the stairs'; 'Zlatko, put your slippers on'; 'Don't drink cold water' and other such cautions. They would say all this with care expressed in their faces, never raising their voices, not even when Zlatko made mistakes. It was a blanket of love, warmth and kindness. At night, when the three of them were alone at home they would pamper him with their excessive care and over protection. His father would massage his bad leg, for this not only warmed up his leg, but his whole body as well, creating a feeling of well-being.

Listening to his friends stories and often visiting their homes, Zlatko realised that life in their families was completely different from his own. This caused dissatisfaction with his family. He just wanted to be an equal among his friends and would gladly take some of the 'difficulties' of their lives, just to be equal to them. They would often say so to him, 'I bet you're spoilt at home and never get a spanking either.' Zlatko was offended by this, although the boys meant it as a compliment. He would get a little angry with this, but hid his anger for fear of losing his friends.

When the war broke out in Bosnia, it created many problems for everyone by bringing hunger, fear, sorrow, cold and darkness in its wake. Zlatko lost many friends, some moved to other countries and many simply went to more protected parts of the city. He missed them and the games he used to watch greatly. Only a few of his friends were left and they could not go out and play because their parents feared for their lives. Many parents took their children to the cellars where they spent whole days and nights.

Zlatko's parents also tried to talk him into going down into the cellar and told him that there was enough space to play. He was determined otherwise, 'I'm not a mouse, I don't want to go into the cellar.' He said there was a horrible smell down there which would suffocate him and not enough light because he could not stand darkness. Zlatko had a lot of other reasons and always concluded by saying, 'I am not going down there and that's that!'

As the war went on the atrocities increased. The shelling killed more and more of his friends and neighbours, leaving corpses strayed in the street, at the cross-roads and in bread queues. His parents took a harder stance and forced Zlatko into the cellar. It was probably the safest shelter from death. Zlatko was angry at first, but when he realised that his anger was to no avail - his parents preferred him to be angry than killed - he gave into their wishes silently. Night time was more difficult because they could not massage Zlatko's bad leg, which they considered to be an important medical procedure, particularly because it made Zlatko happy and relaxed. Realising this, Zlatko's parents found it harder each time to decide to go to the cellar. They would have preferred if someone else made the decision for them, but everyone was preoccupied with their own family and how to survive the shells which killed more and more men, women and children every day. Time went by monotonously with more and more shells killing civilians. The shells were indiscriminate in their destruction. Two winters had left the citizens of Sarajevo starved, cold, exhausted and frightened.

One night, Zlatko told his parents he did not want to go to the cellar, 'I want to sleep in my bed in my room. You go if you want, I'm not scared. Just make sure you lock the door.'

Of course they did not want to leave him alone, but he had been becoming increasingly restless, uncomfortable and adamant. The cellar gave him nightmares and he pleaded to sleep in his room just for this night. Ten minutes before midnight a mortar, fired from the hill, hit Zlatko's house. His parents heard the explosion from the cellar. They tried to reassure themselves, 'It couldn't have hit Zlatko's room...it must have hit the kitchen.' Still, they rushed to Zlatko's room thinking he would be upset and scared, and because they wanted to bring him into the cellar before any more mortars landed on their house.

Darkness, smoke and dust were emanating in thick puffs from the entrance of Zlatko's room. Pieces of furniture and toys were strewn everywhere. They scrambled their way to Zlatko's bed. The mortar had hit his bed and he was wounded; very badly wounded. They did not even have time to comfort him or to tell him not to be afraid for he was dying. Zlatko's father tried to massage his bad leg, to encourage him. Zlatko only quietly said, 'It's all over Dad...you don't have to do that anymore.'

'I'll take you to the hospital, my son, don't you worry.' The tears ran down his cheeks. There was nothing he could do. He realised that Zlatko would never be referee again.

SVRAKE CONCENTRATION CAMP

ào

AT EARLY DAWN, Vejsil heard knocking at the door. 'Who is it?' he asked, surprised at who would be outside at this time. 'It's me, Risto, your neighbour.' His voice was agitated. Vejsil recognised the voice and unlocked and opened the door.

'How come you're so early? Is something wrong?'

His neighbour Risto's face twitched in an effort to avoid eye contact. 'Get ready quickly!' he ordered.

Vejsil realised from the tone of Risto's voice and the three men behind him with guns that his Serb neighbours had come to take his family away. He had already heard of surprise attacks taking place in other neighbourhoods, but he had not expected the same in his own village. Perhaps he should have fled with his family earlier, instead of being proud and refusing to run away from his own home. Now he did not know what would happen to them.

'Where are you taking us?'

Risto did not reply, he only stared at Vejsil and then started examining Vejsil's flat, overturning furniture in his haste. The noise had woken up his little children, who came running into the room wide eyed.

'Uncle Risto, what are you doing here?' they asked innocently.

There was an uncomfortable silence and Risto became even more agitated. The children, sensing the tension, were becoming scared and one of them started crying. Risto became impatient and motioned to them to get out. Leaving the flat Vejsil glanced for the last time across the children's room. His family had lived in this village for generations and his house was for him a record of his family history, as if it was the cover of a history book and his family were the pages. It was for him a

symbol of their continuity. Now, his home, vacated of its inhabitants, became an empty husk; the pages of history were being torn out of the book.

Vejsil and his family were bundled into a bus and taken to a Serb detention camp, situated in the former Yugoslav Army service plant at Hadzici, with other Muslims from their village. When they reached the camp, Vejsil was separated from his wife and children. He did not know where they were taken. New people were being brought into the camp everyday, some of them were killed immediately, others taken in unknown directions. Only a small number were kept inside. Some of the Muslim civilians captured in surprise attacks in their homes were told that they would be exchanged for Chetniks captured by the Bosnian Army in the battlefield. Vejsil, too, was told that he would be used for exchange, but he was not sure whether or not to believe the Serbs. One day he was taken to one exchange point at a mountain ridge near Kobiljaca with some other Bosnians. However, they spent the whole time wet and shivering, in the rain and snow, their skeletons rattling in the wind like some bizarre cartoon, only to be returned to the same camp without the exchange taking place.

Three months later Vejsil was moved from Hadzici to the notorious camp in 'Svrake' near Vogosca. Vejsil was kept there for a hundred days. For a hundred days he had to endure abuse, humiliation and beatings: they kicked him, beat him with iron rods, heavy logs and anything else they could lay hands on. Nursing his own wounds, he wished he could block out the noise of the sufferings of other inmates. With every scream he could feel the pain being inflicted on those around him as if it were himself being tortured. Even worse was the sense of impotence. In particular the cries for help he heard from the Muslim women and girls being raped and tortured. Their screams and cries for help would wrench his stomach. He wondered what his wife was enduring and he thanked God that he had no daughters. Perhaps it would have been better if his wife just died, if she was being tortured like this. Then what would become of his little sons, if they became motherless? And he thought of Risto, how he had transformed from their helpful neighbour into a torturing criminal overnight. 'What had snapped in his psyche all of a sudden? Or was the good neighbour act all those years a mere facade? Why does he begrudge my existence? What have I done to him to deserve this?'

Vejsil can still hear the cries for help that rang through the camp, when E.I., a young student, was repeatedly raped on an upper floor. The Serbs had captured her in Ilidza and subjected her to incessant torture and humiliation. He still feels guilty about not trying to help her, although he knew that the strength of eight fully armed Chetniks could not be matched by an exhausted, hungry and maltreated man.

He also vividly recalls a woman called Djulsa, who had been in hiding with a Catholic family in Otes, before the Chetniks found her. He did not know what had been done to her and her three daughters and son at the Svrake Concentration Camp, but it had affected her mind and driven her insane. Mentally unstable and in desperate need of counselling, she was vulnerable not only to the Serbs, but even to herself. It was also upsetting and disturbing for the other inmates who were already under considerable strain.

Vejsil had been contemplating an escape from the camp, but a real chance never came. One rainy afternoon in the late autumn, a Chetnik named Perica ordered Vejsil to carry a trunk of ammunition for him. 'Where is he going at this late hour?' Vejsil asked himself. On leaving, another Chetnik told him, 'He's taking you out to kill you. Don't worry Turk, Perica is a skilled slayer, he'll finish you off quickly.' Perica added, 'Don't try anything foolish, Turk.' They followed a winding track; Vejsil did not know the terrain, so Perica gave the orders of movement. Night was falling and rain mixed with snow followed. Vejsil felt the intensifying humidity and cold. Suddenly, out of the darkness, a deep male voice called, 'Who goes there?'

'Prisoner.' Vejsil responded quickly.

'Put down what you're carrying!'

As soon as he did so, the shooting started. He could not see in the darkness where the shots came from. He felt his left thigh jerk. It started bleeding heavily. Losing his balance and utterly exhausted he fell to the ground and passed out.

When he regained consciousness he could only hear some remote rifle fire which soon died down. He heard movement in the higher branches of the trees and the flapping of wings, as the birds flew away. Vejsil crawled slowly into a hole in a tree trunk for some shelter. It offered little comfort, but at least he was safe from view and could rest. 'I didn't have this much security in the camp,' he thought. His wound was bleeding and hurting and he was losing his strength, but increasingly he felt something previously unknown to him: an instinct of endurance and persistence. The night and the cold, however, were hard and the wound hurt unbearably.

He lost and regained consciousness several times. Whenever he was awake, he was afraid of losing his identity and forgetting all about

75

himself, so he repeated aloud, 'I am Vejsil K., a professor from Hadzici. I was a prisoner of the Chetniks at the Svrake Camp and I was freed by the soldiers of the Bosnian Army...' He presumed that his liberators had lost orientation in the dark and rainy night and had been killed. 'God forbid that those young and healthy boys should die for me, me with this seriously heavy wound which I might not survive.' He hoped that someone would find him, dead or alive so those thugs would never touch him again.

The night had been long and his periods of unconsciousness lasted longer and longer. Whenever awake, he repeated facts about himself, but now in his head for he could not speak anymore. Periods of waking seemed to last only seconds. The cold of early dawn woke him up. He heard steps on dry leaves under the snow. He was relieved that someone was coming, but perturbed that it could be Serbs and he would be captured again. He was too weak to escape and realised that they had seen him. The two young men approached him and one of them said, 'Hey are you one of us?' Vejsil confirmed by nodding his head. Happiness overwhelmed him; happiness mixed with anxiety for he might be dreaming. He was revived by the realisation that he was saved. The soldiers took him to an earth-cabin where he was washed and his wound was bandaged. 'Am I really so lucky?' Vejsil wondered; he still could not speak due to his weakness and happiness. He was moved to the hospital in Sarajevo and could hardly believe that he was in a clean hospital bed being attended to by courteous staff and not confined in that torturous camp.

A month after he was brought to the hospital, Vejsil was informed that his wife and sons were saved too, they were alive and in a safe place. His own and his family's escape melted into one single happiness - the joy of being reborn and the hope of a new, peaceful life.

THE HIDEOUT

ैं

THIS ACCOUNT was relayed to me by a young Bosnian soldier, no more than twenty years of age. He was badly wounded and had been evacuated to Sarajevo. The day after he told me about Ahmed and Hajrija I returned to find him no longer there. I was told he had been transferred to another medical facility, perhaps abroad; I suspect he had passed away during the night and the doctors felt it better not to tell an elderly lady such sad news.

*   *   *

Hajrija and Adem lived in a little village at the end of the forest, near the town of Foca. They were honest, quiet and modest people, who did not expect much from life. Their first two children, daughters, had married before the war. One had settled in a little town not far from the village and the other in a village three hours away from the family home. When the war started, Hajrija was grateful to God that her daughters were married.

Their village had suffered in the Second World War when the Chetniks committed similar atrocities as now. Her father-in-law, who died five years ago, had not forgotten to his dying day the crimes committed and the suffering he had endured. He used to tell Hajrija how he had escaped when Chetniks burned his house to the ground during the War, leaving only the stone foundation. They had taken everything, everything except the iron plough.

When the war started, Hajrija soon realised that the bloody history of her people was repeating itself. She too remembered how the Chetniks had killed all the people of the neighbouring village and she

77

and her family had become refugees at a very early age. Knowing the dangers that could befall them, this time Hajrija took precautions to try and ensure their safety. She was not worried for herself, but for Ahmed, her youngest son, so she dug a hole in the ground right at the beginning of the war. It was big enough for her eleven year old son to hide, but only up to his neck. His head would stick out to prevent suffocation. The hole was covered with two mattresses and an old bench. There were also a lot of other pieces of old furniture, clothes and pottery scattered around to hide the boy in case of an emergency.

One day she heard Chetniks hammering at her door. She sent Ahmed to his hideaway and told him not to come out under any circumstances. Within a few minutes of his crawling into the little cellar underneath the house, she watched as the door was broken down by three Chetniks. They were her neighbours and they were drunk. Their bloodshot eyes were scanning the walls and doors of the front room. She froze with fear; first her cheeks, then hands, and then her legs seemed glued to the ground.

'Who else is in the house, you bitch?' they demanded.

Hajrija told them her husband and sons had left the house at the beginning of the war, and that she knew nothing about their whereabouts. Her daughters had married men in far away villages before the war, and she had not heard about them since the war started. She did not know whether they were dead or alive, or where they had been sent.

The Chetniks were unconvinced and repeated their questions. 'Who are you hiding, eh? Talk! You're not mute, you Turk bitch! Don't think you can fool us!' They were becoming impatient and increasingly aggressive. 'Stop wasting our time...you obviously haven't heard about us. You'll bloody well remember us when we've finished with you!'

Hajrija repeated what she had already told them, everything she knew about her family. She was shaking with fear. Marko, one of the Chetniks, swore at her, stripped off her shawl and slapped her hard twice. She fell to the ground. 'Think you can fool us? You think you are smarter than us?' He hit her on the head with his rifle butt.

'Cut her throat, Marko. She'd like that because she would go

78

straight into Turk paradise! C'mon, hurry up, why are you talking to her?' said Mihajlo and laughed nastily.

'No. Don't kill her right away, we don't want to screw a corpse,' added the younger Chetnik, almost a beardless boy.

Hajrija was silently praying that Ahmed would not be discovered. She tried to hide her anxiety and her fear for Ahmed's life. How successful she was, she did not know.

They started dancing around her and even on her in a bizarre Indian-like ritual. 'Get up right now! Come on, get up and watch the celebration. You don't want to miss this, do you?' said Marko setting fire to Hajrija's house with a burst of incendiary bullets.

'You see, you Turk bitch, you see how good we Chetniks are, only the house is burning now, but we'll think of something for you as well, there's plenty of time,' said Mihajlo, who had not finished his sentence when Ahmed crawled out of the house, black in the face. He started running towards his mother coughing and spluttering, but was brought to a halt by the butt of a rifle.

'Oh, look at this sweet, little lamb. We haven't had this much fun in three days,' the Chetnik with a big black moustache said and got up from the pile of rocks and bricks he was sitting on.

'Come on, come on, sweet lamb.' Old Mihajlo's giggling horrified Hajrija. She was alone with the child amongst these killers. There was not a friendly soul anywhere, the whole village had burned down; only herself and Ahmed, still a child, and three murdering Chetniks.

Hajrija realised there was no way out, and started quietly calling death to save her from these monsters.

The Chetniks now started singing, grabbed Ahmed and led him to a tree stump, laughing loudly.

'And now the real fun is beginning.'

Old Mihajlo ran towards the tree stump and ordered Ahmed to put his head on it, not paying any attention to Hajrija any longer.

'It's not going to hurt a lot, little Turk, don't be afraid.'

This was followed by a burst of laughter among the Chetniks. Like a skilled cattle cut-throat, one of the Chetniks decapitated Ahmed with one move of an axe. Ahmed's head rolled all the way to Hajrija's legs. The blood from the veins of his neck sprayed her, while she lay on the

ground horrified.

The Chetniks having had their fun, and no longer interested in Hajrija, disappeared. Their drunken voices trailed off into the forest.

The next day, a Bosnian Army unit came to the village and decided to spend the night there. All they found in the ghostly empty village of burnt down houses and stables was a completely grey-haired woman, all curled up in a corner. She was whispering to herself. The soldiers came closer to hear what she was saying. She did not pay any attention to the newcomers and continued to whisper. It was difficult to understand her at first, but eventually, after patient questioning, the soldiers were able to put together the chronology of the bloody events that happened the day before.

Hajrija sat in the same forlorn position gazing at her lap. She started singing an old lullaby and swaying with the melody. Then she waved her hands at something invisible as if to send somebody away, but the gestures were very gentle, as if she was gesturing to a baby or somebody very close. Sometimes the movements of her hands were fast and furious as though she was defending herself from wild animals. She talked for a long time and then she became tired and her voice became weaker and weaker, until only her lips were moving and her voice was inaudible.

Suddenly she jumped up and astonished everybody with a piercing scream. Her eyes were transfixed on the pear tree outside where the boy's head was hanging from the branches. Noticing the decapitated head and torso outside, a party of soldiers were dispatched to bury the body. After the short funeral Hajrija started cursing the murderers again, using all the known and unknown curses that came to her lips. She was now sobbing hysterically and tried to strangle herself. When she did not succeed, she grabbed the bloody axe lying near by.

The soldiers rushed to stop her and prevented the disaster in time. Later Hajrija began to search every corner of her burnt down house, desperately looking for something. Eventually she found a huge stone and tried to smash it against her head, but again the soldiers managed to stop her from harming herself.

After this Hajrija started whining in a sad voice, 'Where are my sons, my heroes? I can't find you, my three sons, my three golden apples? Did the Chetnik murderers kill you the way they killed your mother? My beautiful sons were killed by the neighbours, may they never walk on this earth again.'

The images of her lost sons loomed up before her: all three of them, together with a long dead woman, her neighbour, whose only son died when he was very young. Then she turned to the soldiers with a look of surprise, as if she saw them for the first time.

'And you came to see the Chetniks chop my head off like a chicken. I heard everything, absolutely everything. I heard the Chetniks axe cut my head off and saw my head rolling far from the tree stump... I heard everything. As long as my Ahmed is alive. Those murderers don't fear God so they tried to do the same to Ahmed, to decapitate him, but I wouldn't let them. No, no mother would let them; they wouldn't chop his head off as long as his mother is alive, no, no, never as long as I live.'

Hajrija went silent and just looked in front of herself, staring vacantly. Exhausted, she refused the food and water the soldiers offered her. The soldiers then walked away from her so as not to disturb her further. A little later they put Hajrija to bed in a makeshift army bed.

The next morning the soldiers did not find Hajrija in her bed and after a short search they found her lying dead on the grass.

NEZIR'S PREMONITION

❧

'I DON'T WANT TO BE MOVED to a Sarajevo clinic. I can be treated here just as well.'

A little later Nezir added, less agitated, 'You are as good as the doctors in Sarajevo, you all studied from the same books.'

'But we don't have the medicines we need and our operating rooms are under-equipped, especially for more complicated operations.'

'My wounds will heal without an operation.'

'You shouldn't wait too long Nezir, your condition is getting worse everyday. You must have the operation as soon as possible.'

'I said no. You can't force me.'

'We wouldn't even think of it, but we are just stating the facts.'

Such conversations between Nezir and the doctors at the Mostar hospital occurred everyday, without progress. Nezir was adamant. His leg had been amputated up to the knee and did not show any signs of healing. His condition was deteriorating and he was suffering from high fevers and tremors. At the same time the pressure on him to agree to the transfer was growing from both the doctors and his family.

Still Nezir refused to be persuaded. He could not part from his eighteen year old son, who was fighting in the war from the slopes of Mount Velez. Being in Mostar meant he could see his son more often; the distance between them was not so great. Sometimes his son would come to see him and go back to the front-line all in the same day. More importantly, being close to his son, he felt he somehow protected him from harm. He worried about Mustafa, 'He is only a child still, not even nineteen yet…fighting somewhere on the front-line.'

Nezir's presence in Mostar was all the more important because he was haunted by a bad premonition, a vision of tragedy. He never told anyone about his feeling. He could not explain it to himself either and though he never discussed it with any one, his wife knew. The nagging fear was so great that in his mind this trip to Sarajevo would be fateful and somehow precipitate the catastrophe. And if anything terrible were to happen, he wanted to be there. His wife tried to console him, but even she herself was becoming scared.

Though Nezir had been a sensible and sociable man, he was always ready for a joke, even if his tendency to joke was diminishing with age. He was becoming more anxious and cautious now. He found a myriad of pretexts to stall his move, 'We are getting old,' 'I am not as quick as before,' but the reality was that he would lie awake night after night thinking about his prescience, wondering where it was coming from. He knew it happened to other people, but he could not explain this phenomenon to himself.

'Maybe some inner truth had risen from the depth of my being. But why?' Nezir asked himself repeatedly. One day he thought about dreams. 'Maybe,' thought Nezir, 'a man dreams a bad dream and it frightens him. He wakes up and forgets about it, but some fear, some pain, remains and finds its place in man's soul, and later tortures him with bad premonitions.'

'It must be a kind of illness otherwise everybody would have had it,' he concluded. He wondered if there was such a thing as a 'happy' premonition. It was a vicious circle that offered no answers.

He was fighting his thoughts inside and the transfer to Sarajevo outside. His wife, a sensitive woman, saw the change in him and guessed his deepest troubles, that he was having these visions and was expecting something bad to happen. It was haunting them both day and night. They could not rest, not even in their sleep. They lived in dread of a tragedy in the family and worried in solitude.

Worn out from the mental exhaustion and constant fear, Nezir's reasons for staying were eventually knocked down one by one, until eventually he agreed to the move. The transfer was vital for his survival and his son had urged Nezir incessantly until he gave in.

A date was set and everything was ready for the transportation to Sarajevo. The army commander had organised and secured the trip

over the snow-covered mountains. Nezir was scheduled to leave at 4pm in order to travel as far as possible before darkness.

However, only a day before, Nezir's son, Mustafa, was killed on the slopes of Mount Velez. Nezir's worst fears had come true, but the pain of loss was not softened by its anticipation. He could not understand why he, an invalid, was still alive, while Mustafa, full of youth, with his whole life ahead of him, should be taken away. The irony galled him.

'How can I live without my son?'

He felt he had no right to be alive and the idea of trying to save his life seemed pointless. What was he to live for now? He had spent his whole life for his son, raising Mustafa with love and care. He was proud of his boy and was now waiting for Mustafa to marry and play with his grandchildren.

'I'm to be cured and my young hero is to be buried.'

His son's funeral was set for 5pm, an hour after Nezir's departure was scheduled, after sunset so that the people at the funeral would be safe from enemy shelling. The proximity of these two totally unrelated events brought into focus how random and senseless human tragedy is. The world is spinning and you never know where the pin of the wheel of tragedy will stop and whether it will hit you.

'May your son rest in peace. He died for our nation with courage and sacrifice; he died trying to defend us all. He is a hero, but you must continue with your recovery, Nezir,' they told him.

Despite all his protests, Nezir was persuaded to the move, for there was nothing to keep him in Mostar any longer. The stretcher party finally set off and while they were carrying him through the plains, he stifled his tears. However, when they reached the mountains, the dam holding back Nezir's sorrow burst at last. He covered his face with a handkerchief so that he would not have to see the mountain that took his only son. Then he asked the stretcher bearers,

'Stop for a minute, they are burying my son right now, stop so his father can see him for the last time, although he is dead and I'm so far away from him.'

The mountain echoed from Nezir's sobs, 'I'm going to be cured and my hero is being buried. How am I going to live without my son?' There was no reply. The stretcher bearers were crying too, but hid their tears.

'Slow down! This is my mountain - this is where my son fought the war,' Nezir cried.

The silence of the mountain was disturbed by gunshots somewhere in the distance, the snow being ground under-foot and Nezir's sobs. The stretcher bearers were taking turns.

'Why wasn't it me instead of my child? Not even death likes old men,' he lamented. The stretcher bearers did not respond to Nezir's sad monologue and continued the journey in silence.

One of them skidded on a steep icy mountain path but regained his balance very quickly.

'If only you had thrown me into the ravine,' said Nezir. 'I would have been very grateful.'

At the entrance to our Sarajevo clinic Nezir again broke down. A heavy pain stabbed his chest, taking all his strength from him. The tears and words had dried up; his pain became an unbearable agony. He was silent all the time, only answering questions briefly.

'I lost my son and my leg. The wound will heal, but the grief of my dead son will never go away.'

A gush of sadness permeated the whole room, like the roar of a huge waterfall; it was a dominating, wordless, stirring up of emotions that one could not escape.

'You can never get over the loss of a child. It is like thousands of shells have made a hole in your heart and you can't fill the void. I don't know what to do. My son is always on my mind, I see him in front of my eyes when I am awake and when I talk to you. It seems like I don't want to lose sight of him. It's not an apparition, it's my desire to always have him with me. You know, I even talk to him sometimes in an unknown language, that's why he is always close to me. He will be with me as long as I live, otherwise I could not survive without him.'

THE BLOOD ON
ABDURAHMAN'S FEET

ट्रॐ

BEFORE DAWN Abdurahman was awoken by the sound of
shooting. He was surprised. 'Maybe the neighbours are going
hunting,' he thought, but he could not hear the dogs barking.
'Are they celebrating something?' he wondered, but he did not recall
his Serb neighbours having any early morning celebrations before.
'Maybe they're chasing a thief.' He remembered that two years ago an
off-licence, owned by his neighbour Savo, was broken into. Savo had
chased them with his gun and had broken the leg of a young man from
the village. This young man had had his leg in a cast for a long time and
could not walk again without a stick. 'Anyway,' thought
Abdurahman, pulling the covers over his head, 'It's none of my busi-
ness what other people do.'

He had heard that in some other villages a bit further from theirs,
Serbs were persecuting and killing any Muslims they came across.
However, there had been no tension in this area. They were all living in
harmony. After all, they had grown up together. Why would they be
after his blood? His family had no quarrel with them. Rubbing his
eyes, Abdurahman went back to bed. His wife had gone with the children to visit her mother, so he was alone at home.

He had not even fallen asleep, when he heard the booming of
drunken voices, 'Out! Out Balija! (a derogative term) We're gonna cut
your throats, you sheep!' Others were adding, 'Slaughter all the Turk
cattle, we don't need them; we have our own cattle.'

The smell of smoke was wafting in through the small window of the

88

summer kitchen. Jumping out of bed, he saw that they had set fire to his neighbour Juso's house. 'What has happened to everyone in the neighbourhood? Have they gone mad?'

He thought about running away, but there was shooting from all sides and he could not find a safe way out. Before he could work out what to do, a bearded Chetnik with a gun had broken down the door of his house, and was now standing inside.

'Give me your gun and get out of here,' he demanded, seething with hatred.

'I don't have a gun,' Abdurahman replied, stunned.

'Don't lie, you Turk bastard.' The Chetnik rammed the butt end of his gun into Abdurahman's head knocking him out.

When he regained consciousness, Abdurahman's nose was bleeding and there was a roaring pain in his head. He was in a van that was rattling up and down the hills. He felt like vomiting as the vibrations of the van, along a rough village road, reverberated through his bruised body. He felt even worse every time the van swung round the bends in the road. The van was overloaded with frightened people, in silent dread. As the van lurched, there were groans of pain from the Bosnians who had been beaten by the Chetniks: battered then loaded onto the van. The Chetniks had fixed plastic covers to the sides and back of the van so that their victims would not know the direction in which they were travelling, but they were left with a good idea of their destiny.

Finally the van jolted like a wild horse and stopped abruptly at Omarska Concentration Camp. Abdurahman felt nausea sweep over him as he stood before the camp, a cesspit of death and torture. The barracks were overcrowded with beaten, wounded and disabled people. He noticed that some of the victims had crosses branded on their chests or backs by hot iron. Eyes had been torn out by Chetniks, and mutilated faces were forced to drink bottles filled with old, dirty motor oil in one go. Although physically abused and unable to retaliate, people were beaten over and over again with poles, spades, boots and anything that came to hand. The most difficult part of it all was to watch and wait.

The emaciated inmates, ribs protruding through their taut skins, were gradually starving to death and searched rubbish bins to alleviate their hunger and despair. They would fall upon anything that the disgusting, dirty Chetniks had thrown away. The disgust was irrelevant when hunger was tormenting them day and night. The proverb, 'Hunger doesn't have eyes' was true. 'Why are we keeping ourselves alive for slaughter by the Chetniks?' thought Abdurahman.

Exhausted and deformed, suicide seemed a reasonable option to many. It offered a release from the despair, the indignity and the sheer horror of their situations. This torturous existence was so far removed from their previous lives, that they found it difficult to comprehend the change. However, if the Chetniks suspected somebody of suicidal intention, they would target him for constant abuse and punish him severely. They reserved the right to kill solely to themselves.

The death machine, unceasing in its determination to wipe out all traces of their existence, took fully loaded vans and buses of Bosnians for execution night after night, bringing back fresh groups of Bosnians into the empty barracks to replace the recently murdered victims. At night the Chetniks would come to the barracks with lists, reading out names and taking out large groups of Bosnians for execution. This bloody game had been set up by the Chetniks long before Abdurahman and his neighbours were hurled into this dark cycle of death. Now the death game was accelerating. Many Bosnians had become mentally unbalanced by the wait, but disability, physical or mental, did not exempt them from being killed. Rajko, a Chetnik from one of the Kozara villages would often say, 'I can't sleep as long as these Turks are alive even if they are mad.'

One night Abdurahman's name was on the execution list together with about a hundred and fifty other Bosnians. They came out of the vans into a field, presumably the execution place. The group was halted at the edge of the field, surrounded by a dense chain of Chetniks with their guns, all ready to open fire. Abdurahman racked his mind on how to escape. There was no way out; they did not stand a chance of surviving if they attempted to run and if they just stood there they would be riddled with bullets. There was only one thing to do and he murmured it to the men next to him, 'As soon as you hear the first shots, fall to the ground.' The men paralysed by fear were too terrified to grasp Abdurahman's advice or react. They awaited death frozen and helpless, except Becir, who, like Abdurahman, realised that there was no other escape than falling to the ground as soon as the shooting started and pretending to be dead before being shot.

Within seconds the dance of death began as the Chetniks let rip with their weapons with no evident signs of mercy or remorse. Abdurahman and Becir fell quickly to the ground. Immediately they felt the heavy burden of corpses falling upon them. Very soon another difficulty arose: the danger of suffocation from the blood which was pouring abundantly from the dead bodies. They had to dig through the tunnel of dead bodies to reach the surface and avoid suffocation. But for a while they had to lie under the corpses, as crawling out would have been perilous. The woods were not far, and if there was a Chetnik hiding there, he would not have let them escape.

After a while they got up and each saw his own ghostly reflection in the other, the shocking image of a ghost painted in blood. They could hardly believe that they had survived the shooting and were still unsure whether they would make it to free territory alive. They had no time to be astonished by their escape, so they embraced each other and separated, deciding to take different directions for safety.

Abdurahman picked his way over the dead, bloody bodies of his compatriot martyrs. Questions surged into his mind, 'How can I leave these dead compatriots of mine, innocently killed cousins, neighbours and friends? How can I leave them alone without a last prayer, without a funeral? Is it a betrayal?' he asked himself. 'But I can't stay here,' he said, continuing his silent monologue, 'I'll die from hunger.' His sadness was overwhelming, 'Where can I go?' He cried for a long time until his tears ran dry. Then he bid farewell to the noble martyrs and recited the opening chapter of the Qur'an, the Fatiha, praying God would have mercy on their souls. Abdurahman left the terrible scene and began to walk in a south easterly direction.

He suffered a lot during those wandering days, hungry, bloody and haunted by visions of the executions. He wandered across rivers and streams. He had to catch fish and ate them raw to avoid starvation. In the woods he found some wild apples and pears to supplement his meagre diet. He washed himself in a stream and tried to wash his bloody clothes, but without much success. The difficult journey and hunger exhausted him so he would sleep at dusk, hiding himself in hollow trees because it was quite warm. When there was no other choice he would sleep in a field. Gradually he was wasting away and his eyesight was getting weaker. At dusk or at dawn it would seem to him that shrubs and trees with low branches were Chetniks waving menacingly at him.

After about twenty days he came to a small village. A mosque stood in isolation with its minaret showing signs of recent shelling and attempted destruction. It was early in the morning and there were no signs of people or even animals. Abdurahman was suddenly overtaken by spasms of giddiness; his legs were shaking, he was losing balance and there was a drumming noise in his ears.

'I'll call here to get some proper sleep. Just a chance to have a few hours of uninterrupted sleep.' It was early morning and that gave the village an appearance of desolation and abandon. He stumbled and tottered to the first house and crashed down on the doorstep, falling fast asleep. He cannot recall how long he slept, but he remembers being awakened by the soft voice of an old woman, 'My hero... are you hungry?'

'Yes, I am hungry, but I'm not a hero,' and after a pause quietly added, 'I feel as if I've risen from the dead.' The old woman looked puzzled by these words and decided that he was so tired he did not know what he was saying.

'Is it possible to rise from the dead?' the old woman asked curiously.

'If she knew what I've been through she would understand me,' he said to himself.

'You look famished. I wish I could give you something, really I do, but the Chetniks have taken everything away. We managed to hide in the woods and saved ourselves, but the enemies have taken everything. All I have is this egg. My hen laid it this morning,' she said offering him a boiled egg. 'If you want to sleep you can use my sofa.' She indicated to a wooden sofa inside. 'But I'm afraid I haven't got any blankets. I can cover you with a washed potato bag and my woolly jumper. You will be warm.'

Abdurahman thanked her and accepted the egg, but did not stay. Waving goodbye, he glanced back at the woman. Her face was wrinkled, but her eyes gazed at him warmly. She seemed uncommonly calm, despite being entirely alone. 'Her face is difficult to forget,' thought Abdurahman as he walked away. However, twenty days of hunger and exhaustion could not be cured by one day's rest and one boiled egg.

Abdurahman hurried on to look for his freed compatriots. Eventually he arrived at the doorstep of the first police station he encountered. Policemen, neighbours and elderly people surrounded him and were all visibly excited and delighted to see him. Old Omeraga grasped Abdurahman's hand and said, 'You look as if you have risen from the dead.' Abdurahman smiled and said, 'I have indeed, thanks to Allah.'

Abdurahman was transferred to a hospital for medical treatment where I met him and tried to help him overcome the psychological trauma of his bloody ordeal at Omarska and the harrowing journey to freedom. As shelling continued and persecution increased, with his own bruises to remind him of his torture, no trauma unit could make him forget the suffering of innocent Bosnian people in Omarska Concentration Camp.

As time went on, Abdurahman would recount what had happened to him. Whenever he relayed details of what he had seen and experienced there, including his own escape from death, he would turn pale. Horrible scenes were etched in his memory. People listened to his every word.

'You know, I trod upon the bodies and blood of my closest relatives and best friends. I trod upon the dead to reach freedom. There was no other way to save myself, believe me.'

They all believed him. It seemed clear to everyone, except Abdurahman himself, that he had been branded by the concentration camp and it had obviously affected his stability, self-reliance and self-confidence. He meditated for a while and then took off his socks and stared at his feet.

'Even now you can see stains of the martyrs' blood on my feet. Oh yes, indeed, I can still see the blood of the martyrs' on my feet. I haven't washed their blood off, and Allah only knows whether I will ever manage to do so.'

ATTEMPTED MURDER

※

'IT SEEMS AS IF THEY HAVE forgotten about us,' said Ramiz jokingly to his friend who was minding the machine gun they had between them.

'They haven't, Ramiz, they know it's never too late.'

'Don't call for bad luck. You weren't like that before!'

'Neither were you!'

They continued to joke with one another for a while, pricking their ears to the roaring of enemy aircraft flying above Mount Vlasic.

Tall, blonde and blue eyed, Ramiz often cracked jokes, trying to keep his spirits up, as well as those of his friend who, while not very talkative, was amused by Ramiz's jokes and would even laugh at them. The laughter kept them going.

'We're a good team,' Ramiz thought, 'I joke and he laughs. Thank God he does. Otherwise life would be unbearable around here. If we didn't laugh, I think we'd slit our wrists because things are so bad sometimes.'

Nevertheless, Ramiz's spirit began to sink as night approached. Dense snow flakes were falling thick and fast on the frozen mountains and the cold was biting.

'I'm so cold; if I were blind I'd think I was stark naked,' Ramiz thought to himself, not wanting to tell Jusuf in case he agreed and started to complain himself. 'Then we'll have had it. If we start whinging then our whole pretence that things are fine will break down.'

A loud roaring of explosions and the constant whizzing of shells distracted him. Ramiz raised his head and followed the path of the fire blazing in the sky. His eyes were transfixed on the night sky and from his observation he anticipated danger. He said nothing to Jusuf at first, but, realising that the shelling was worse than any they had experienced so far, he thought he ought to warn him subtly.

'They must have heard me because they're shelling targets near our position. I always knew they liked us!' They laughed together.

At that moment, a shell fell a couple of metres away from them. The snow came down on them in a gush, pieces of frozen snow scratched their faces and a pine branch broke off nearby.

'Now we have a bit of greenery as well. Didn't I tell you they're taking good care of us?!' The next shell took the words right out of his mouth.

Ramiz cannot remember how long he was unconscious. He thinks that the cold helped him regain consciousness soon after. His head was buzzing and he could not immediately recall what had happened. His whole body was racked in pain, especially his head, both legs and right arm. Completely feeble and immobile, Jusuf was lying a little below his legs and Ramiz could hear him groan.

He heard some voices approaching and realised that people were nearby. Ramiz moved his head to the right and noticed two bearded enemy soldiers quite close. He could just distinguish their conversation and can remember one of them asking, 'How shall I kill them? Should I shoot them or hit them on the head with the butt end of my gun?' The other replied, 'No, we need them for exchange,' adding, in a whisper, 'Apparently one of our senior officers has been captured, the one called Duke. We need these two to bargain for the exchange of Duke.'

By this time they were right next to Ramiz and Jusuf. They now stopped speaking. Without a word, they carried Ramiz between them to a nearby sledge and set off down the hill to a lower plain. Here, he was transferred to a van. He did not know what happened to Jusuf and whether he would ever see him again. The van, in which Ramiz was, drove slowly, but it jostled a lot, causing him a lot of pain in his head and legs. He had completely lost feeling in his right arm and could not move it. It just hung down limply. They drove for a long time, and Ramiz was not able to express this 'long time' in units. It seemed never ending. The bumpy pace at which they travelled intensified his pain. He slipped in and out of consciousness until they eventually arrived in Banja Luka, the largest Bosnian town held by the Serbs.

Ramiz was placed in a military hospital ward which contained three beds. Two severely injured enemy soldiers were lying in the two other beds. They were so heavily rolled up in bandages that he could hardly see their faces. 'Maybe their limbs have been amputated,' thought Ramiz. The two soldiers moaned continuously, calling for nurses and asking for pain killers and on one occasion one of them even asked for poison. 'Give it to me to die at once, I can't stand it anymore, I can't, I really can't.' They cursed all the time, mostly their army but one of them once even cursed the mother who gave birth to him.

Despite the pain he was in, an interrogation followed immediately: questions about the situation on the front-line and about his army unit. These were questions Ramiz, as a soldier, could not answer truthfully. His interrogators realised this and after almost every investigation they concluded, 'You speak very well, if only you didn't lie.' Ramiz would say to himself, 'Of course I'm lying. I'm not a traitor.'

During the two days in Banja Luka hospital he was questioned without a break; when one group of interrogators had finished, another one would take over and so on until he was exhausted. Ramiz grew dizzier with every new investigation and he feared making a mistake. Above all he feared answering the same question differently to the various investigation officers.

A policeman was always present in the room to ensure Ramiz could not escape, though there was hardly any chance of that considering his injuries. Ramiz still felt pain in every part of his body, especially his right leg. All the bones in his legs was broken in several places, he had sporadic headaches and the pain in his legs was incessant. He lay stiff as a corpse because any movement, however slight, caused him unbearable pain. Yet his pride, understandable even to himself, prevented him from asking for help from them, from the enemy. His rational inner voice would say, 'You're wounded and helpless, you have to be cured, there will be more battles...the war isn't over,' but his unquestioning pride was stronger than any reasoning or pain which tortured him. They put a very strong cast on his right leg, while his right arm was left to hang limply; he could not move it at all, not even any of his fingers.

He was tormented by the pain and worried also about what had happened to Jusuf. His own prospects did not look good. Although they had said they would exchange him for their officer, Ramiz did not trust them. He was uneasy about it and would ask himself why they were keeping him in hospital. In the eyes of the Serbs, he was the enemy and would very often tell himself, 'Well, they can kill me anytime they like, I'm in their hands.' This nagging doubt was strong, always present, making him uneasy.

Only the nurses, doctors and a few visitors ever entered the room where Ramiz and the wounded enemy lay. Some of these visitors would make fun of him, others would insult him, but they would not approach the bed. Probably because of the ever present policeman. 'They can't be trusted, I have to watch out,' Ramiz reminded himself constantly and would try to stay awake as long as possible at night.

On the third day of his stay in Banja Luka Hospital Ramiz's fears became a horrible reality. In spite of the policeman, a Serb employee of the hospital felt so much hatred towards Ramiz that he attacked him. It was all pre-meditated. First, a young woman entered the room and started a conversation with the policeman. She positioned herself so that the policeman had his back towards the door unable to see the entrance to the patients' room. Then, two men entered the room. Ramiz sensed that something bad was looming and within minutes he saw the blade of a knife plunging towards him. He raised his left arm to protect his head and neck. However, his right arm, completely immobile, could not do anything at all. As the blade descended it slashed the unprotected veins on the right side of his neck. Blood gushed forth from his neck as if a ram had been slaughtered.

The entire police team on duty nearby gathered in the room to see what was happening, but a sense of urgency was grotesquely lacking. Some of them, amused to see the blood pouring from his neck, were smirking. He was taken down to the operating theatre. However, when he arrived there, the surgeon lingered, unconcerned about the bleeding. Almost casually he asked, 'Can you see me?'

'Yes,' Ramiz replied weakly.

'That's lucky for you. If you had said you couldn't see me, I wouldn't have bothered operating. I would have left you to bleed to death.'

'Only then did they transfer me from the stretcher onto the operating table, where they stopped the bleeding and carried out the operation and stitched the severed veins in my neck,' Ramiz recalled.

However, on regaining consciousness after the operation he felt a terrible roaring of blood as if there were waterfalls in the veins of his neck. He asked the doctor about it, but the doctor remained silent. He only repeated what he had said before the operation, 'Be thankful you're alive. I could have left you to bleed to death. I didn't have to do this operation.'

That day he was transported to Prijedor Hospital and told he was needed for an exchange. This time it actually took place. Nine days later, he was swapped and the Bosnian Army drove him immediately to our clinic. The treatment in the Sarajevo clinic was, in a relatively short time, quite successful. During the course of this treatment, we discovered that he was in pain because his artery had been deliberately reconnected to his vein. Another operation to correct the surgical stitching in his neck - artery to artery and vein to vein - was planned. 'I've heard that the operation is a difficult one, but I'm not worried now that I'm with my own people.'

He can now lift his right arm a little in a sign of greeting. Having learnt that his family had survived, he was simply happy to be alive and with them. Sadly, he never heard of what happened to Jusuf.

Smiling even after recounting his sad story I remember him once saying, 'I'm only thankful to Allah for saving my life and my mind.'

Official Bosnian statistics record that by the end of 1995, 156,824 people were known to have been killed, the vast majority being Muslims, of which 16,854 were children. 75,259 were registered wounded, of which nearly 50% (34,712) were children.

Evidence of wide-scale 'ethnic cleansing' was overwhelming, for example the following cities now no longer have any Muslims residing there - figures in brackets indicate the pre-war population percentage: Foca (61%), Rogatica (60%), Visegrad (63.4%), Vlasenica (55.3%), Bratunac (64.2%), Srebrenica (72.9%), Zvornik (59.4%), Prijedor (44%) - the list goes on.

Over 25% of Bosnians are now refugees in over 100 countries (1,245,000 out of a pre-war population of nearly 4.4 million), with a further 763,224 displaced within Bosnia Herzegovina.

Source of statistics: Prof. Smail Cekic/Institute for Research into Crimes against Humanity and International Law (Sarajevo, 1996)